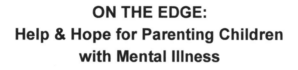

ON THE EDGE:
Help & Hope for Parenting Children
with Mental Illness

By Andrea Berryman Childreth

On The Edge

Published by Spotlight Marketing
ISBN 978-1-7335919-0-4 (paperback)
ISBN 978-1-7335919-1-1 (ebook)

www.OnTheEdgeBook.com

ACKNOWLEDGEMENTS

The author and publisher would like to thank Dr. Ross Greene for his permission to share the principles of his groundbreaking communication approach as part of this book.

I am so thankful for my supportive husband, Jeff, daughter, Sophia, parents, Jim and Lindsay Berryman, in-laws, Ray and Jan Childreth, and my sisters, Kelly Berryman and Kristina Fischer, who have all been my rock during our journey.

Also, to the families who shared their stories for this book, I honor your courage and will forever appreciate your vulnerability.

Finally, the deepest gratitude and admiration goes to my daughter, Chloe, who has boldly and unselfishly shared her story in order to increase awareness about youth mental illness and help other families.

ON THE EDGE

TABLE OF CONTENTS

Foreword 1
Prologue: Our Story 3
Chapter 1—What's Going on with My Kid?!? 9

Part I: Diagnosis and Treatment of Mental Disorders in Youth. 17

Chapter 2—Diagnoses: Common Mental Illnesses, Symptoms,
Causes & Treatments 19
Chapter 3—Related Conditions 73
Chapter 4—Treatment Options... 95

Part II: Practical Tips... 107

Our Story Continues… 109

Chapter 5—Finding Help…and Paying for It 113
Chapter 6—Hospitalization 129
Chapter 7—How to Help Your Kid 137
Chapter 8—The Trouble with School.. 155
Chapter 9—Your Child's Social Life, Social Media, and Social
Perils 169
Chapter 10—The Justice System 181
Chapter 11—Relapse and Recovery 189
Chapter 12—Caring for Yourself and Your Family 197
Chapter 13—Change Must Come 207

Our Stories Go On 213

Resources 220
Endnotes 225

Foreword

Did you know that 20% of teens are affected by some type of mental illness? Did you know that 25% of adults experience a mental illness during their lives?

This means that everyone knows someone who is struggling with a mental health disorder. Everyone! We should not be ashamed to talk openly about something that touches all our lives. We should not be ashamed about something that is no one's fault. And, certainly, we should not be ashamed of our children. After all, kids don't want to misbehave. They want to be good. They are just doing the best they can with the tools they have, and it's our job to help them find the most effective tools so they can be their best selves.

I wrote this book to share family stories—my stories and the stories of other families. Through our experiences of struggles and triumphs, challenges and lessons, I hope that other parents who face similar situations will benefit from our education, knowledge, and resources. As more people learn about these illnesses and the difficult journeys parents and children face, I hope that, one day, our society will embrace mental illness for what it is—an uncontrollable brain disease that must be managed by medication and therapeutic guidance, just like any other chronic diseases of the body.

Knowledge is power. Please join me and others in improving our knowledge so we can fight against the stigma and shame associated with mental illness.

RISK OF SUICIDE

If you or someone you know is in an emergency, call The National Suicide Prevention Lifeline for free at 1-800-273-TALK (8255) or call 911 immediately.

Prologue: Our Story

How had it come to this?

We were prisoners in our own home. Our daughter Chloe routinely exploded with foul language, tantrums, and even threats with weapons, and her younger sister had become her minion and punching bag. Alienated from neighbors and peers, Chloe had no friends and her days consisted of sleeping until about noon, eating, and playing video games until the wee hours of the morning. She wasn't growing, except in size as she gained nearly forty pounds. Disabled by anxiety and depression, unable to communicate or socialize with her sixth-grade classmates, or to break down school assignments into manageable tasks, she often refused to get out of bed and cried uncontrollably when I tried to get her to go to school. She attended only about a third of the time, and more often than not, I had to go with her for support. Our school district did little to provide resources and help, and my husband and I felt demoralized and defeated. We despaired about Chloe's future and what we imagined it would be…

Chloe had been a beautiful, bright baby with big blue eyes and a quick smile that drew everyone's attention. Although she was an active baby, she was fairly easy to keep in a routine and soothe when she got upset. During my pregnancy with our second daughter, Sophia, I had noticed that Chloe was willful, but my husband Jeff and I weren't overly concerned about any of her behavior. After Sophia was born, eighteen-month-old Chloe was quite jealous and would often come and whack her baby sister on the head while I was breastfeeding. But it didn't seem like unusual behavior for a jealous big sister.

When we enrolled her in a local Montessori preschool at age three, we really started to notice the contrasts of her behavior. The teacher reported that Chloe didn't follow instructions well during circle time, and she never played with other kids. During recess, Chloe would always be alone with the school bunny in the corner of the playground and when she did interact with the other kids, she didn't know how to share and play with others.

After a few months at the preschool, Chloe would cry hysterically when I dropped her off, clinging to me desperately when I struggled to get out the door. An emotional wreck, I would drive to work, bawling all the way as I wondered what we were doing wrong. Finally, during winter break, Jeff and I decided to pull her out of the school. We felt that we couldn't continue to leave our four-year-old child distraught every day, but we also worried that we were failing as parents because we had given in to her hysterics.

As Chloe got older, her tantrums continued and intensified. Having grown up with "old school" parenting skills, we saw that using these techniques only seemed to make things worse and we felt helpless, always on the brink of crisis. We didn't know how to handle her unmanageable mood swings and rages.

During a parent-teacher conference, Chloe's first-grade teacher told me that Chloe needed the teacher's one-on-one guidance for all class assignments. Chloe's eyes were usually glazed over during lessons and the teacher was certain that Chloe wasn't processing or comprehending information and instruction given to the entire class.

Early on, I had my suspicions that Chloe was struggling with a mental illness. I have bipolar disorder and suffer with anxiety and depression myself, so when I saw familiar symptoms in Chloe, I recognized them. I knew what she was suffering because I had experienced it myself. So when the teacher recommended that we have Chloe evaluated, we took action. Her pediatrician referred us to a psychiatrist, and soon,

Chloe was diagnosed with bipolar disorder, anxiety, depression, and ADHD.

I was relieved. I knew that she could be treated and she would be okay.

The doctor prescribed medication to help stabilize Chloe's moods and temper her rages. Although the medication helped on and off, it seemed as if we were still on a constant rollercoaster of emotional swings and unpredictable moods.

After a few years, we switched doctors, but one thing remained constant—the roller coaster of various medications and Chloe's rages. She struggled with impulse control and it was hard for her to follow our rules. We took life day-by-day but, at one point, we were so desperate for answers that we took Chloe to a city five hours away from our home to get third and fourth opinions from yet another psychiatrist and psychologist.

The psychologist reported that Chloe was healthy and that we were making up issues that she didn't have but the psychiatrist diagnosed Chloe with Asperger's Syndrome, a high-functioning form of autism. The psychiatrist forwarded this diagnosis and her evaluation to our local doctor, suggesting appropriate treatments. But our doctor didn't agree. Asperger's can often be misdiagnosed and frequently has comorbid diagnoses—and Chloe's symptoms weren't obvious—so our doctor refused to accept the diagnosis. She insisted that Chloe was only bipolar.

Confused, defeated, and frustrated, we plodded through the weeks, months, and years. By the time Chloe was in the sixth grade, my eleven-year-old daughter refused to attend school. Day after day, she'd curl up in a fetal position on my bed, rocking back and forth and crying like a primal animal. "No, Mama," she'd wail. "Pleeease, I can't." I heard this mantra day after day and, yet again, I'd call her school to let them know that Chloe wouldn't be coming.

Chloe felt like a failure on multiple fronts. In a classroom of more than 35 students, she had severe issues with overstimulation and sensory problems that dominated her fragile mind and focus, so she could not perform well academically. Uncontrollable anxiety sent her into a deep depression. She was unable to identify and interpret social nuances—body language, facial expressions, tone of voice, and sarcasm—but she was quick-witted enough to feel shunned. Bullying left her constantly feeling confused, defensive, and combative. Not surprisingly, she refused to go to school, and when she did go, I needed to accompany her to help her manage her anxiety, break down assignments, communicate, or socialize with her peers.

Our school district didn't help. They didn't have the appropriate staff to manage a student like Chloe, and they offered few resources and little support. They ostracized and blamed us for poor parenting and flat-out lied to us about Chloe's federally-mandated legal rights as a public school student. We were forced to hire legal representation before the district provided Chloe with psychological testing and a homebound tutor.

At home, I was overtaxed and exhausted—emotionally and physically—from coping with my mentally ill daughter with little refuge other than my parents and in-laws. Struggling with my own mental health challenges, I was often a raw heaping mess of emotions and tears. Jeff and I had grave doubts whether Chloe would be able to complete high school, much less graduate, attend college or trade school, and contribute as a productive member of society. Our despair about her future continued to grow with each day.

By the end of Chloe's sixth-grade year, I fortunately shared my story with a colleague, who told me that her grandson attended an alternative charter school. I immediately called the school and was relieved and thankful to learn that the new school would understand her special needs, and they would work with her to maximize her learning capabilities. I enrolled Chloe for seventh grade. Although she felt reluctant and anxious when she started in the fall, Chloe actually liked her school for the first time *ever*. While she was still guarded with the other students, by the end of her seventh grade year she started to trust the school and the kids and, finally, she made a few friends and invited them over to our house. It was a *huge* accomplishment!

Still, her new school wasn't enough to change her warped perception of life and the dysfunctional behaviors she had used over the years to survive. She was still skipping school half of the time.

And she was still ruling our household.

Constantly looking for options, Jeff and I visited a residential treatment center and decided to send Chloe to inpatient treatment. It was the most difficult decision we ever made.

Sending Chloe to treatment for her mental illness mere weeks after her thirteenth birthday was the budding of my blog, "Bipolar Lemonade."

I started the blog as a form of therapy to help me deal with the guilt and anxiety I felt from sending Chloe four hours away to inpatient care in what felt like prison conditions. It was also a way to share with my friends and family that our seemingly normal, "picture-perfect" family had mental illnesses. My husband Jeff, a dentist, was the son of retired teachers and I am a marketing consultant with a father who is a retired physician and a mom who had been our city's mayor. No one would have guessed the "secrets" that lurked behind our walls.

With each post I wrote and shared on Facebook, I was filled with anxiety. What would people think? What might they say about me and my family?

But the results were inspirational. Friends and family who weren't affected by mental illness were generous with their support and admiration of my courage and efforts. Many others came out of the woodwork, mostly privately, to share their stories of mental illness, struggles, and despair. People I had never met friended me on Facebook so they could read my blog updates and share their stories with me.

After Chloe returned home from treatment and began to show real progress, it hit me that I needed to share these other stories, to talk about the shame and stigma of what is so often swept under the rug, to let other parents know that they are not alone and there is help.

Just as importantly, I became convinced that early diagnosis is the key to successfully treating and managing a mental illness. Identifying a mental illness *before* a youth turns eighteen can potentially save that young adult from years of mischief, misery, and legal turmoil. Early diagnosis and intervention mean a youth—with the help of parents—has time to accept it for what it is, to find a medication regimen that balances the brain, and to learn how to effectively manage life and its triggers.

I believe to my core that this is the key to preventing profound consequences down the road, and to saving our American taxpayers millions of dollars in escalating health care costs, incarceration, and justice resources. Our system is broken, and change must come. But, for now, you can make a difference in *one* child's life. Your child, your son or daughter deserves your acceptance and your advocacy. I'm here to help you on that journey.

Chapter 1—What's Going on with My Kid?!?

If you have a child who is extremely difficult to raise, with or without a diagnosed mental illness, you've probably heard every piece of advice out there...

> "Have you tried putting him in a time-out?"
> "Just take away his favorite toy until he behaves!"
> "Have you locked him in his room until he stops throwing a fit?"
> "You need to take away the TV until he stops that behavior."
> My favorite is, "I would never tolerate that kind of behavior in *my* house!"

Such remarks may make you want to cry, scream, run away ... or all three.

If only it were that easy!

You've probably already tried every trick in the book and every tip on the internet, and you've absorbed advice from family, friends, teachers, counselors, and doctors. You've probably also felt confusion, frustration, helplessness, and more—because, at some point, it likely became crystal clear that no one seemed to understand the enormity of your daily challenges and crises. You might have started to feel ostracized and misunderstood. Or you might think you are a horrible parent.

But you're not a horrible parent, and what you're going through is not your fault. The fact that you are open to reading this book demonstrates that you are a proactive and deeply caring parent! You are ready to learn some critical information that will help your child and your family move forward and change your circumstance.

Parenting a child with mental illness, or suspected mental illness, begins with your willingness to reach out for support, to ask questions, and to persevere. To do these things, we've got to let go of some of our own hang-ups—the social and cultural expectations that concern us—and opt to do what's best for our children and our families. Let's face it, mental illness carries with it a huge amount of stigma. It's not easy to admit that there's something wrong with your daughter's brain that makes her paranoid. It's not easy to explain that your son can't leave the house because he is anxious and depressed. It's not easy to let people see your child obsessing about germs and washing her hands two-hundred times a day. But when you can let go of how others might judge you and your child, you can become an effective advocate for your child.

A "Difficult" Child or a Mentally Ill Child?

Half of mental health conditions begin by age 14 and three-quarters develop by age 24. But, sometimes, mental illnesses can be hard to spot. A young child may seem willful, or parents and teachers may assume that a behavior problem is a matter of discipline or personality. What's more, in adolescence normal changes in personality and behavior may mimic or mask symptoms of a mental health condition. At all stages, parents' early engagement and support are crucial to improving outcomes and increasing the promise of recovery.

It's hard to consider—much less admit—that your child may have a brain disorder. People rarely talk about mental illness and when they do, such conversations often reference bad events or even tragedies covered in the news. It's no surprise that with images and stories that sweep across society, media coverage chronically stigmatizes mental illness.

Friends, family members, teachers, and strangers perpetuate the stigma in interpersonal ways, too. Playmates might tease a challenging child, whom adults might label as a "bad apple" or a troublemaker. Sadly, these labels stick with a person for life, sometimes creating serious problems down the road. But it's important to know that kids don't want to be "bad." They want to do the best they can with what they have—mental capacity, family influences, and role models—so it is important to give difficult children all the tools they need to be the best person they can be.

As with any medical disease or disorder, the first step to a healthy outcome is a thorough and accurate diagnosis. Accepting that your challenging child may have a mental illness is a positive start, and if you and your doctor identify that your child does indeed have a mental illness, chances are good that it can be treated so that your child can live a "normal" and productive life. In reading this book, you are taking a great step for your family.

Some Important Information to Know

Severe Mental Illnesses Are:

- Biological brain disorders that interfere with normal brain chemistry. Genetic factors may create a predisposition in some people, and life stresses may trigger the onset of symptoms.
- Very common. In any given year, approximately 25 million Americans are affected. More than 7.5 million children and adolescents suffer from these illnesses.
- Equal opportunity diseases, striking families from all walks of life regardless of age, race, income, religion, or education.
- Co-morbid. Typically, mental illness comes with more than just one diagnosis (i.e., bipolar disorder, anxiety, depression, ADHD).
- Devastating to the ill person's family. All family members are affected as the ways they think, feel, and relate are frequently disrupted, seriously reducing the ability to live a normal life.
- Treatable! Appropriate medical care and rehabilitation enable many people to recover enough to live productive lives.

A mental illness is a condition that impacts a person's thinking, feeling, or mood and may also affect their ability to relate to others and to function on a daily basis. Each patient will have different experiences, even with the same diagnosis. In any case, recovery—including meaningful roles in relationships, school, and work—is possible, especially when treatment starts early and parents play a strong role in the recovery process.

Research suggests that multiple, interlinking causes combine to influence whether someone develops a mental health condition. These include genetics, environment, and lifestyle. A stressful home life or traumatic life events (such as being the victim of a crime) may make some people more susceptible. Also, biochemical processes, circuits, and basic brain structure may play a role. But one thing is clear: A mental health condition is not the result of one event.

Severe Mental Illnesses Are Not:

- Anybody's fault. They are not caused by poor parenting or weak character.
- Preventable or curable at this time. Great advances have been made in understanding brain functioning, but not enough is known yet to prevent or cure serious brain disorders (mental illnesses).
- Hopeless! These illnesses present difficult challenges but help is available. Support, education, and a community of friends who understand can make family life satisfying and meaningful again.

How Do I Know If This Is a Mental Illness?

For many parents, the challenge is to grasp what is "typical" youth behavior—seen as "difficult," "challenging," or "willful"—versus behavior that warrants a psychiatric evaluation. The first step is to listen to your child, pay attention to symptoms, and consider these questions:

- Do you have a family history of mental health issues?
- Are behaviors or symptoms significantly disrupting your child's life or yours?
- Is your child miserable?
- Is your family miserable?

- Is your child engaging in behaviors you don't condone?

Regardless of your internal banter, if you answer yes to any of these questions, schedule an appointment with a psychiatrist for an evaluation immediately.

You might not know what behaviors or symptoms are worrisome. Red flags include:

- Unexplained headaches and stomachaches.
- Sadness that lasts two weeks or more.
- Withdrawal that lasts two weeks or more.
- Inability to communicate or interact with others.
- Overwhelming, unwarranted, or intense worries, stress, or fears that interfere with daily life.
- Difficulty focusing, paying attention, or sitting still.
- Poor performance in school.
- Hyperactivity.
- Drastic changes in behavior or personality.
- Severe, extreme, or problematic mood swings.
- Impulsive behavior.
- Preoccupation with food and weight.
- Loss of appetite, loss of weight, frequent vomiting, or use of laxatives.
- Substance abuse.
- Self-injury or self-harm, such as cutting or burning.
- Expressing a desire to badly hurt others.
- Dangerous, violent, or out-of-control behavior.
- Psychosis (losing touch with reality).
- Suicidal thoughts or attempted suicide.

One of the clearest signs that something might be wrong is when your child tells you that it might be. Don't take too lightly any comments they make about feeling a need for help. Consider:

- Has your child expressed a desire to seek help?
- Have they been contacting online support groups or searching for information about mental illness?

- Has your child expressed confusion over what is "wrong" or "different" about them?
- Has your child sought help online or from a school counselor, friend, or elsewhere?

If you're seeing any of these signs in your child, what are your next steps?

- **Validate any expressions of a desire for help.** This is so important! If your kid is asking you for help or seeking it elsewhere, they need it! It's critical that you not minimize the situation or the child's feelings. Most kids do not want to be different from their peers, and because of the shame and stigma associated with mental illness, few will want to admit that they need help.
- **If your child asks for help, provide it.** Schedule an evaluation with a psychiatrist or see your pediatrician and ask for a referral.
- **Don't let your own baggage get in the way of finding help for your child.** Especially if you have a mental illness, it's easy to feel guilty and to blame yourself for the torment your child may be experiencing, but it is not your fault. If your child had diabetes, you wouldn't withhold diagnosis and treatment, right? Mental illness is an uncontrollable brain disorder. Regardless of the specific causes or the nature of the illness, your child deserves medical attention and a successful, happy future.

A Few Cautions for Parents

Take Care of Yourself, Too

If your child or teen has a mental illness or is experiencing of any of the above symptoms, you need to talk to your pediatrician and probably get a referral to a psychiatrist. But you also need to take care of yourself. I suggest these steps to help you get educated and get support:

- **Trust your intuition and gut.** If something doesn't feel right about what a doctor or another professional says, don't settle. Ask your questions, express your doubts, push for answers, or get another opinion. You are the advocate.

- **Get educated.** A great place to start is the National Alliance on Mental Illness (NAMI), which provides classes, information about local resources, tips, a hotline, and a variety of other supports. NAMI has 1,000 affiliates across the country. You can find the national organization at www.NAMI.org.

- **Get support.** Advocacy and support groups can be informative, empowering, and comforting. NAMI and my organization, Bipolar Lemonade, provide several advocacy options and support groups. You can find many other local support groups and advocates online and in many states and counties.

- **Ask for help.** Taking care of a mentally ill family member will suck the life out of anybody. It can drain you of your own emotional, mental and physical resources. If you don't have the bandwidth to deal with daily chores, errands, or other responsibilities, hire someone or ask a friend or family member to help you out.

- **Try to be good to yourself.** If you feel good, you'll be able to think clearly and take better care of your ill child and other family members. Pay attention to the basics—nutrition, exercise, healthy sleep—and try meditation, therapy, time with friends, or whatever makes you feel refreshed, strong, and positive.

Part I: Diagnosis and Treatment of Mental Disorders in Youth

As our story, and the stories of many others, demonstrates, getting an accurate diagnosis of a child's mental illness can be a drawn-out process. There might be many pieces of the puzzle that need to be identified and put together to describe, and accurately treat, your child's mental illness. This section is here to help you become familiar with some of the more common diagnoses and their treatment options.

Each child is different and can present unique combinations of their behaviors so this is not a comprehensive list, nor is it intended to be used to diagnose your child. But in becoming familiar with the range of illnesses and possible treatments, it may prove to be a resource to help you talk with your care team about your child and learn some of the language and vocabulary of mental illness.

Chapter 2—Diagnoses: Common Mental Illnesses, Symptoms, Causes & Treatments

ADHD

Attention deficit hyperactivity disorder (ADHD) is a condition which is characterized by inattention, hyperactivity, and impulsivity. ADHD is most commonly diagnosed in young people, according to the Center for Disease Control and Prevention (CDC), and can be confused with other mental illnesses that have similar characteristics. An estimated 9% of children between ages three and seventeen have ADHD. While ADHD is usually diagnosed in childhood, it does not only affect children. An estimated 4% of adults have ADHD.

With treatment, most people with ADHD can be successful in school and work, and lead productive lives. Researchers are using new tools such as brain imaging to better understand the condition and to find more effective ways to treat and prevent ADHD.

Symptoms

While some behaviors associated with ADHD are normal, someone with ADHD will have trouble controlling these behaviors and will show them much more frequently and for longer than six months.

Signs of inattention include:

- Becoming easily distracted and jumping from activity to activity.
- Becoming bored with a task quickly.
- Difficulty focusing attention or completing a single task or activity.
- Trouble completing or turning in homework assignments.
- Losing things such as school supplies or toys.
- Not listening or paying attention when spoken to.
- Daydreaming or wandering with lack of motivation.
- Difficulty processing information quickly.
- Struggling to follow directions.

Signs of hyperactivity include:

- Fidgeting, squirming, and having trouble sitting still.
- Non-stop talking.
- Touching or playing with everything.
- Difficulty doing quiet tasks or activities.

Signs of impulsivity include:

- Impatience.
- Acting without regard for consequences.
- Blurting things out.
- Difficulty taking turns, waiting, or sharing.
- Interrupting others.

Causes

There are several factors believed to contribute to ADHD:

- **Genetics.** Research shows that genes may be a large contributor to ADHD. ADHD often runs in families and some trends in specific brain areas that contribute to attention may have a genetic basis.
- **Environmental factors.** Studies show a link between cigarette smoking and alcohol use during pregnancy and children who have ADHD. Exposure to lead as a child has also been shown to increase the likelihood of ADHD.

Diagnosis

ADHD occurs in both children and adults, but is most often diagnosed in childhood. Getting a diagnosis for ADHD can sometimes be difficult because the symptoms of ADHD are similar to typical behavior in most young children. Teachers are often the first to notice ADHD symptoms because they see children in a learning environment with peers every day.

Doctors do not have a test that can diagnose a child with ADHD, so it is important to provide a doctor or mental health professional with all the necessary information that might relate to the diagnosis. Caregivers will need to ensure that a child is otherwise healthy and rule out medical problems and any other causes for symptoms, such as environmental changes or difficulty in school.

Related Conditions

Similar to adults with ADHD, about two-thirds of children with the disorder also have another condition. Conditions that are commonly associated with ADHD include the following:

- Learning disabilities.
- Oppositional defiant disorder: refusal to accept directions or authority from adults or others.
- Conduct disorder, persistent destructive or violent behaviors.
- Anxiety and depression.
- Obsessive-compulsive disorder.
- Bipolar disorder.
- Tourette's syndrome.
- Sleep disorders.
- Bed-wetting.
- Substance abuse.

When a child suffers from symptoms related to other conditions, it can complicate the treatment for ADHD, making it more difficult. Therefore, to increase the effectiveness of treatment for ADHD and any additional disorders, it is important to work with a skilled professional to establish accurate diagnoses and effective treatment.

Treatment

ADHD is managed and treated in several ways:

- Medications, including stimulants, non-stimulants, and antidepressants.
- Behavioral therapy.
- Self-management, education programs, and assistance through schools or work.

ANXIETY DISORDERS

Everyone experiences anxiety. Driving in heavy traffic is a common source of anxiety, but that feeling also keeps us alert and cautious so we'll drive carefully and avoid accidents. Speaking in front of a group makes most of us anxious, but that anxiety motivates us to prepare and do well. However, when feelings of intense fear and distress are overwhelming and prevent us from doing everyday things, an anxiety disorder may be the cause.

Anxiety disorders are the most common mental health concern in the United States. About forty million adults in the U.S., or 18%, have an anxiety disorder. Approximately 8% of children and teenagers experience the negative impact of an anxiety disorder at school and at home, and most people with anxiety disorders develop symptoms before age twenty-one. Women are 60% more likely to be diagnosed with an anxiety disorder than men.

Types of Anxiety Disorders

Different anxiety disorders have different symptoms, and each type has its own treatment plan. The most common anxiety disorders include:

Panic Disorder

This disorder is characterized by panic attacks—sudden and unexpected feelings of terror—that sometimes strike repeatedly and without warning or reason. Often mistaken for a heart attack, a panic attack causes powerful, physical symptoms including chest pain, heart palpitations, dizziness, shortness of breath, and stomach upset. Many people will go to desperate measures to avoid having a subsequent attack, including social isolation or avoiding going to specific places, and often have prolonged periods (at least a month) of worrying about losing control or experiencing another attack.

Phobias

Everyone tries to avoid certain things or situations that make them uncomfortable or even fearful. However, for someone with a phobia, certain places, events, or objects create powerful reactions of strong, irrational fear. Most people with specific phobias have several triggers. To avoid panicking, someone with specific phobias will work hard to avoid their triggers. Common phobias in children include fear of animals, storms, heights, water, blood, the dark, and medical procedures. If they can't avoid their phobias, children will experience anxiety which might be obvious in crying, tantrums, clinging, avoidance, headaches, and stomachaches. The fear and attempts to avoid it can seem to take over a person's life.

Generalized Anxiety Disorder (GAD)

Generalized anxiety disorder produces chronic, exaggerated worrying about everyday life, so a child with GAD will worry about grades, friendships, sports, families, and everything else. This can consume hours each day, making it hard to concentrate or finish routine daily tasks. A child with GAD may become exhausted by worry and experience headaches, tension, or nausea.

Social Anxiety Disorder

Unlike shyness, this disorder causes intense fear of social and performance situations, such as having a teacher call on the student in class or being required to perform in front of peers. Also known as social phobia, this fear is often driven by irrational worries about social humiliation, such as "saying something stupid" or "not knowing what to say." A child with social anxiety disorder may become isolated while avoiding conversations and be unable to contribute to class discussions or offer their ideas. As a result, socialization, relationships, grades, and even school attendance may be affected. When social and performance situations cannot be avoided, children with social anxiety disorder will commonly react with panic attack symptoms.

Separation Anxiety Disorder

When a parent leaves the room or goes away, separation anxiety is normal in a child under three years of age or when first being left in a new environment. Usually, these feelings subside when the child is distracted. But separation anxiety disorder may be diagnosed when an older child (most commonly seven to nine years of age) is unable to separate from a parent or other family member without prolonged upset. When separated from parents or caregivers—at home or away—children with this disorder may experience excessive anxiety, feelings of misery, and extreme homesickness, as well as headaches or stomachaches. These children commonly worry that something bad or terrible will happen to their parents or caregivers while they are apart, so they may refuse to separate, experiencing great distress when they have to go to bed alone, attend school, go on playdates, or stay at a sleepover.

Other Anxiety Disorders

Additional disorders include agoraphobia—a fear of certain places or situations that the person believes will be difficult to escape from—and substance/medication-induced anxiety disorder involving intoxication or withdrawal related to medication treatment.

Causes

Scientists believe that many factors combine to cause anxiety disorders:

- **Genetics.** Some families have a higher-than-average number of members experiencing anxiety issues, and studies support the evidence that anxiety disorders run in families. This can be a factor in a child developing an anxiety disorder.
- **Stress.** A stressful or traumatic event such as abuse, death of a loved one, violence, or prolonged illness is often linked to the development of an anxiety disorder.

Diagnosis

The physical symptoms of an anxiety disorder can be easily confused with other medical conditions like heart disease or hyperthyroidism. Therefore, a primary-care doctor should first evaluate the child to rule out physical causes. A doctor's evaluation might include a physical examination, interview, and lab tests. After ruling out a physical illness, the doctor may recommend that the child see a mental health professional to make a diagnosis.

Using the *Diagnostic and Statistical Manual of Mental Disorders* (DSM), a mental health professional is able to identify the specific type of anxiety disorder and any other possible disorders that may be involved, such as depression, ADHD, or substance abuse. Tackling all disorders through comprehensive treatment is the best recovery strategy.

Related Conditions

Anxiety disorders can be seen with other mental health conditions, such as:

- Depression
- Substance abuse
- ADHD
- Eating disorders

- Trouble sleeping

Anxiety can often exacerbate these related conditions, so consult a mental health care professional if anxiety begins to interfere with normal activities on a daily basis.

Treatment

As each anxiety disorder has a different set of symptoms, the treatments will also vary. Common treatments are:

- Psychotherapy, including cognitive behavioral therapy.
- Medications, including anti-anxiety medications and antidepressants.
- Complementary health approaches, including stress and relaxation techniques.

AUTISM

Autism spectrum disorder (ASD) is a developmental disorder that affects a person's ability to socialize and communicate with others. ASD can also result in restricted, repetitive patterns of behavior, interests, or activities. The term "spectrum" refers to the wide range of symptoms, skills, and levels of impairment or disability that people with ASD can display. Some people are mildly impaired by their symptoms, while others are severely disabled.

The prevalence rate for ASD is one in sixty-eight children and rising. Awareness of the disorder and improved screening methods have contributed to the increase in diagnoses in recent years. Boys are four times more likely than girls to develop autism, which crosses racial, ethnic, and social backgrounds equally.

Symptoms

Autism symptoms start to appear during the first three years of life. Social by nature, healthy infants normally gaze at faces, turn toward a voice, grasp a finger, and smile by two or three months of age. By contrast, most children who develop autism have difficulty engaging in the give-and-take of everyday human interactions.

Not all autistic children experience symptoms with the same severity, but all people with ASD have symptoms that affect social interactions and relationships, verbal and nonverbal communication, the ability to manage their emotions constructively, and preoccupation with certain activities. Along with different interests, autistic children generally have different ways of interacting with others. Often, parents are the first to notice that their child shows unusual behaviors, such as failing to make eye contact, not responding to his or her name, or playing with toys in unusual, repetitive ways.

Symptoms of autism can include:

- Delay in language development, such as not responding to their own name or speaking only in single words, if at all.
- Repetitive and routine behaviors, such as walking in a specific pattern or insisting on eating the same meal every day.
- Difficulty making eye contact, such as focusing on a speaker's mouth instead of their eyes, as is usual for most young children.
- Sensory problems, such as experiencing pain from certain sounds (like a ringing telephone) or not reacting to intense cold, pain, or certain sights, sounds, smells, textures, and tastes.
- Difficulty interpreting facial expressions, such as misreading or not noticing subtle facial cues (a smile, wink, or grimace) that indicates the nuances of social communication.
- Problems expressing emotions, including facial expressions, movements, tone of voice, and gestures that are often vague or do not match what is said or felt.
- Fixation on parts of objects, such as focusing on a rotating wheel, instead of playing with peers.
- Absence of pretend play, such as concentrating for a long time on lining up toys in a certain way, rather than playing with them.
- Difficulty interacting with peers due to lack of understanding that others have different information, feelings, and goals.
- Self-harm behavior, such as expressing disapproval by head-banging.

- Sleep problems, such as difficulty falling asleep or staying asleep.

Symptoms of autism fall on a continuum, and the learning, thinking, and problem-solving abilities of children with ASD can range from gifted to severely challenged. Some children with ASD need a lot of help in their daily lives. With a thorough evaluation, doctors can make a diagnosis to help find the best treatment plan for each child.

Causes

Scientists have not discovered a single cause of autism. They believe several factors may contribute to this developmental disorder.

- **Genetics.** If one child in a family has ASD, another sibling is more likely to develop it too. Likewise, identical twins are highly likely to both develop autism if it is present. Relatives of children with autism show minor signs of communication difficulties. Scans have also revealed certain abnormalities of the brain's structure and chemical function in people on the autism spectrum.
- **Environment.** Scientists are currently researching multiple environmental factors that might play a role in contributing to ASD. Many prenatal factors, such as a mother's health, may contribute to a child's developmental disorder. And postnatal factors also affect the development of ASD symptoms, included the hotly debated links to certain vaccine ingredients, although no specific environmental factors have been concretely identified to date.

Diagnosis

The genes for ASD have not yet been identified so there is no medical test to determine the possibility of developing autism. Specialists make the diagnosis after screening for social deficits, communication problems, and repetitive or restricted behavior.

Diagnosing autism is often a two-stage process. The first stage involves general developmental screening during well-child checkups with a pediatrician, who will refer children for additional evaluation if they show certain developmental problems. The second stage involves a thorough evaluation by a team of doctors and other health professionals from a wide range of specialties. At this stage, a child may be diagnosed as having autism or another developmental disorder. Typically, children with ASD can be reliably diagnosed by age two, though some may not be diagnosed until they are older.

Types of ASD Screening Instruments

Sometimes, doctors' screening for autism will ask parents questions about a child's symptoms. Other screening instruments combine information from parents with the doctor's observations of the child. Examples of screening instruments for toddlers and preschoolers include:

- **The Modified Checklist for Autism in Toddlers (M-CHAT)** is a list of informative questions about a child; the answers can indicate whether a specialist should evaluate the child.
- **Screening Tool for Autism in Two-Year-Olds (STAT)** is a set of tasks that children perform under supervision while a specialist assesses key social and communicative behaviors, including imitation, play, and directing attention.
- **Social Communication Questionnaire (SCQ)** is a series of questions parents answer to help specialists determine if a four-year-old child (or older) needs further testing.
- **Communication and Symbolic Behavior Scales (CSBS)** uses parent interviews and direct observations of natural play to collect information on gestures, facial expressions, play behaviors, and other indicators of communication development.

For more information on these screening tools, please visit the website of the Centers for Disease Control and Prevention.

Related Conditions

A child with autism may have additional disorders, which may include:

- **Intellectual disability.** Many children with ASD have some degree of intellectual disability. When tested, some areas of ability may be normal, while others—especially cognitive (thinking) and language abilities—may be relatively weak.

- **Seizures.** One in four children with autism has seizures, often starting in early childhood or during the teen years. Seizures, which are caused by electrical activity in the brain, can result in a short-term loss of consciousness, convulsions, and staring spells. To determine whether a child is having seizures, a doctor will order an electroencephalogram (EEG), a nonsurgical test that records electrical activity in the brain.

- **Fragile X syndrome.** A genetic disorder, Fragile X syndrome is the most common form of inherited intellectual disability, causing symptoms similar to ASD. About one in three children who have Fragile X syndrome also meet the diagnostic criteria for autism, and about one in twenty-five children diagnosed with ASD have the mutation that causes Fragile X syndrome. Because this disorder is inherited, children with autism should be checked for Fragile X, especially if the parents want to have more children. For more information on Fragile X, visit the website for the Eunice Kennedy Shriver National Institute of Child Health and Human Development.

- **Tuberous sclerosis.** A rare genetic disorder that causes non-cancerous tumors to grow in the brain and other vital organs, tuberous sclerosis occurs in 1-4% of people with ASD. A genetic mutation causes the disorder, which has also been linked to intellectual disability, epilepsy, and many other physical and mental health problems. There is no cure for tuberous sclerosis, but many of its symptoms can be treated.

- **Gastrointestinal problems.** Some parents of children with autism report that their child has frequent gastrointestinal (GI) or digestion problems, including stomach pain, diarrhea, constipation, acid reflux, vomiting, or bloating. If a child has GI problems, a gastroenterologist can help find the cause and suggest appropriate treatment.

- **Co-occurring mental illnesses.** Research shows that children with ASD are at higher risk for developing other mental illnesses such as anxiety disorders, attention deficit hyperactivity disorder (ADHD), and depression. Managing these co-occurring conditions can reduce symptoms that appear to worsen a child's disorder. Such management strategies include behavioral therapy, which teaches children how to control their behavior, and medications.

- **Rett syndrome.** Rett syndrome is a genetic mutation-based developmental disorder that, along with specific physical symptoms like the inability to control muscle coordination, includes a regression in development. Children with Rett syndrome develop normally for six to eighteen months before regression and autism-like symptoms appear. However, after this period, most children with Rett syndrome improve their social communication skills, and autistic features are no longer a major area of concern. Unlike autism, Rett syndrome mostly affects girls. One of every 10,000-22,000 girls has Rett syndrome.

Treatment

Autism is treated and managed in several ways:

- Education and development, including specialized classes and skills training and time with therapists and other specialists.
- Behavioral treatments, such as applied behavior analysis (ABA).
- Medication for co-occurring symptoms, combined with therapy.
- Complementary and alternative medicine (CAM), such as supplements and dietary changes.

Though autism cannot be cured, it can be treated effectively.

BIPOLAR DISORDER

A chronic mental illness, bipolar disorder causes dramatic shifts in a person's mood, energy, and ability to think clearly. People with bipolar disorder have high and low moods, known as mania and depression, which tend to be more extreme than the typical ups and downs most people experience. If left untreated, the symptoms usually get worse. However, with a strong lifestyle that includes self-management and a good treatment plan, many people live well with the condition.

During a manic phase, people with bipolar disorder may feel extremely irritable or euphoric. They may experience extremes of behaviors such as agitation, sleeplessness, or talkativeness and, at other times, extreme sadness and hopelessness (depressive episodes). They may also exhibit extreme pleasure-seeking or risk-taking behaviors.

People's symptoms and the severity of their mania or depression vary widely. Although bipolar disorder can occur at any point in life, the average age of onset is twenty-five. Every year, 2.9% of the U.S. population is diagnosed with bipolar disorder, with nearly 83% of cases being classified as severe. Bipolar disorder affects men and women equally.

Early Warning Signs of Bipolar Disorder in Children and Teens

Children may experience severe temper tantrums when told "no," and those tantrums can last for hours while the child continues to become more violent. They may also show odd displays of happy or silly moods and behaviors.

Teenagers with bipolar disorder may show uncharacteristic anger, overconfidence, tearfulness or sleep disruptions. They may experience a drop in grades, quit sports teams or other activities, be suspended from school or arrested for fighting or drug use, engage in risky sexual behavior, or talk about death or suicide. If a teen exhibits these kinds of behaviors, it's a good idea to have a health care provider evaluate the child.

Symptoms

A person with bipolar disorder may experience distinct manic or depressed states, as well as "mixed episodes," in which the person experiences both extremes simultaneously or in rapid sequence. Severe bipolar episodes of mania or depression may also include psychotic symptoms such as hallucinations or delusions, usually mirroring the extreme mood. Someone who is manic might believe he has special powers and may display risky behavior. Someone who is depressed might feel hopeless, helpless, and unable to perform normal tasks. People with bipolar disorder who have psychotic symptoms may be wrongly diagnosed as having schizophrenia.

- **Mania.** To be diagnosed with bipolar disorder, a person must have experienced mania or hypomania, a milder form of mania that doesn't include psychotic episodes. People with hypomania can often function normally in social situations or at work. Some people with bipolar disorder will experience episodes of mania or hypomania many times; others may experience them only rarely. To determine what type of bipolar disorder people have, doctors test how impaired they are during their most severe episode of mania or hypomania.

  Although someone with bipolar disorder may find an elevated mood appealing—especially if it occurs after depression—the "high" does not stop at a comfortable or controllable level. Moods can rapidly become more irritable, behavior more unpredictable, and judgment more impaired. During periods of mania, people frequently behave impulsively, make reckless decisions, and take unusual risks. Most of the time, people in manic states are unaware of the negative consequences of their actions. It's key to learn from prior episodes the kinds of behavior that signal "red flags" to help manage the illness.

- **Depression.** Depression produces a combination of physical and emotional symptoms that inhibit a person's ability to function nearly every day for a period of at least two weeks. The level of depression can range from severe to moderate to mild low moods, which is called dysthymia when it is chronic.

  The lows of bipolar depression are often so debilitating that people may be unable to get out of bed. Typically, depressed people have difficulty falling and staying asleep, but some sleep far more than usual. When people are depressed, even minor decisions such as what to have for dinner can be overwhelming. They may become obsessed with feelings of loss, personal failure, guilt, or helplessness. This negative thinking can lead to thoughts of suicide. In bipolar disorder, suicide is an ever-present danger, as some people become suicidal in manic or mixed states. Depression associated with bipolar disorder may be more difficult to treat.

Causes

Scientists have not discovered a single cause of bipolar disorder. They believe several factors may contribute:

- **Genetics.** The chances of developing bipolar disorder are increased if a child's parents or siblings have the disorder, but the role of genetics is not absolute. A child from a family with a history of bipolar disorder may never develop the disorder, and studies of identical twins have found that, even if one twin develops the disorder, the other may not.
- **Stress.** A stressful event such as a death in the family, an illness, a difficult relationship, or financial problems can trigger the first bipolar episode. Thus, an individual's style of handling stress may also play a role in the development of the illness. In some cases, drug abuse can trigger bipolar disorder.
- **Brain structure.** Brain scans cannot diagnose bipolar disorder in an individual. However, researchers have identified subtle differences in the average size or activation of some brain structures in people with bipolar disorder. While brain structure alone may not cause it, some conditions involving damaged brain tissue can predispose a person towards bipolar disorder and, in some cases, concussions and traumatic head injuries can increase the risk of developing bipolar disorder.

Diagnosis

To diagnose bipolar disorder, a doctor may perform a physical examination, conduct an interview, and order lab tests. While bipolar disorder cannot be identified through a blood test or body scan, these tests can help rule out other illnesses that can resemble the disorder, such as hyperthyroidism. If no other illnesses (or other medicines such as steroids) are causing the symptoms, the doctor may recommend the person see a psychiatrist. To be diagnosed with bipolar illness, a person has to have had at least one episode of mania or hypomania.

The *Diagnostic and Statistical Manual of Mental Disorders* (DSM) defines four types of bipolar illness:

- Bipolar I Disorder is an illness in which people have experienced one or more episodes of mania. Most people diagnosed with bipolar I will have episodes of both mania and depression, though an episode of depression is not necessary for a diagnosis. To be diagnosed with bipolar I, a person's manic or mixed episodes must last at least seven days or be so severe that they require hospitalization.
- Bipolar II Disorder is a subset of bipolar disorder in which people experience depressive episodes shifting back and forth with hypomanic episodes, but never a full manic episode.
- Cyclothymic Disorder or Cyclothymia, is a chronically unstable mood state in which people experience hypomania and mild depression for at least two years. People with cyclothymia may have brief periods of normal mood, but these periods last less than eight weeks.
- "Other specified" and "unspecified" bipolar disorder is diagnosed when a person does not meet the criteria for bipolar I, II or cyclothymia but has had periods of clinically significant abnormal mood elevation. The symptoms may either not last long enough or not meet the full criteria for episodes required to diagnose bipolar I or II.

Patients describe symptoms in a variety of ways, and often this depends on the cultural lens through which the person is looking. In Western cultures, for example, people generally talk about their moods or feelings, while in many Eastern cultures, people refer to physical pain. Research has shown that African Americans and Latinos are more likely to be misdiagnosed, so people who have been diagnosed with bipolar disorder should look for a healthcare professional that understands their background and shares their expectations for treatment.

Related Conditions

Common conditions that people with bipolar disorder also experience include:

- Anxiety disorders.
- Posttraumatic Stress Disorder (PTSD).

- Attention-deficit hyperactivity disorder (ADHD).
- Substance abuse. Many people use alcohol or drugs to try to control their moods or treat their symptoms. Using drugs makes the illness worse and can lead to more frequent relapses and increased suicide attempts.

These related illnesses can make it hard to diagnose and treat bipolar disorder. For example, the antidepressants used to treat obsessive-compulsive disorder and the stimulants used to treat ADHD may worsen symptoms of bipolar disorder and may even trigger manic episodes. But successfully treating bipolar disorder almost always improves these related illnesses, and successful treatment of PTSD, ADHD, or substance abuse usually improves the symptoms of bipolar disorder.

Treatment

Bipolar disorder is treated and managed in several ways:

- Medications, such as mood stabilizers, antipsychotic medications and antidepressants.
- Psychotherapy, such as cognitive behavioral therapy and family-focused therapy.
- Electroconvulsive therapy (ECT).
- Self-management strategies and education.
- Complementary health approaches such as meditation, faith, and prayer.

BORDERLINE PERSONALITY DISORDER

Borderline personality disorder (BPD) is characterized by difficulties in regulating emotion. This difficulty leads to severe, unstable mood swings, impulsivity and instability, poor self-image, and stormy personal relationships. People may make repeated attempts to avoid real or imagined situations of abandonment. The combined result of living with BPD can manifest into destructive behavior, such as self-harm or suicide attempts.

It is estimated that 1.6% of the adult U.S. population has BPD but it may be as high as 5.9%. Nearly 75% of people diagnosed with BPD are women, but recent research suggests that men may be almost as frequently affected by BPD. In the past, men with BPD were often misdiagnosed with PTSD or depression.

Symptoms

People with BPD experience wide mood swings and can display a great sense of instability and insecurity. Signs and symptoms may include:

- Frantic efforts to avoid being abandoned by friends and family.
- Unstable personal relationships that alternate between idealizations ("I'm so in love!") and devaluation ("I hate her!"). This is also known as "splitting."
- Distorted and unstable self-image, which affects moods, values, opinions, goals, and relationships.
- Impulsive behaviors that can have dangerous outcomes, such as excessive spending, unsafe sex, substance abuse, or reckless driving.
- Suicidal and self-harming behavior.
- Periods of intense depressed mood, irritability, or anxiety lasting a few hours to a few days.
- Chronic feelings of boredom or emptiness.
- Inappropriate, intense, or uncontrollable anger—often followed by shame and guilt.
- Stress-related paranoid thoughts and dissociative feelings, which are "out of body" feelings or the feeling of disconnecting from one's thoughts or sense of identity. Severe stress can also lead to brief psychotic episodes.
- Borderline personality disorder is ultimately characterized by the emotional turmoil it causes. People who have it feel emotions intensely and for long periods of time, and it is harder for them to return to a stable baseline after an emotionally intense event. Suicide threats and attempts are very common for people with BPD. Cutting, burning, and other self-harming acts are also common.

Causes

The causes of borderline personality disorder are not fully understood, but scientists agree that it is the result of a combination of factors:

- **Genetics.** While no specific gene has been shown to directly cause BPD, studies in twins suggest this illness has strong hereditary links. BPD is about five times more common among people who have a first-degree relative with the disorder.
- **Environmental factors.** People who experience traumatic life events, such as physical or sexual abuse during childhood or neglect and separation from parents, are at increased risk of developing BPD.
- **Brain function.** Often, in people with BPD, the brain works differently. This suggests that some of the symptoms have a neurological basis. Specifically, the portions of the brain that control emotions, decision-making, and judgment may not communicate well with one another.

Diagnosis

There is no single medical test to diagnose BPD, and a diagnosis is not based on one sign or symptom. BPD is diagnosed by a mental health professional following a comprehensive psychiatric interview that may include talking with previous clinicians, medical evaluations and, when appropriate, interviews with friends and family. To be diagnosed with BPD, a person must have at least five of the nine BPD symptoms listed above.

Related Conditions

BPD can be difficult to diagnose and treat—and successful treatment includes addressing any other disorders a patient might have. A person with BPD may have additional conditions such as:

- Anxiety disorders or PTSD.
- Bipolar disorder.
- Depression.

- Eating disorders, notably bulimia nervosa.
- Other personality disorders.
- Substance abuse disorders.

Treatment

A typical, well-rounded treatment plan includes psychotherapy, medications, and group, peer, and family support. The overarching goal is for someone with BPD to learn what works and what doesn't so that the patient can increasingly self-direct the treatment plan.

- **Psychotherapy**, such as dialectical behavioral therapy (DBT), cognitive behavioral therapy (CBT) and psychodynamic psychotherapy, is the first line of choice for BPD.
- **Medications** are often instrumental to a treatment plan, but there is no one medication specifically made to treat the core symptoms of emptiness, abandonment, and identity disturbance. Rather, several medications can be used off-label to treat some symptoms. For example, mood stabilizers and antidepressants help with mood swings and dysphoria and antipsychotic medication may help control symptoms of rage and disorganized thinking.
- **Short-term hospitalization** may be necessary during times of extreme stress or to ensure safety when the patient is impulsive or suicidal.

DEPRESSION

Everyone experiences occasional sadness or rough patches, especially after difficult life events. Sadness is natural and even healthy, and a temporary "situational" depression is common. But "major" depression or "clinical" depression is more than feeling sad. It's a serious mental health condition that requires understanding, treatment, and a good recovery plan.

With early detection, diagnosis, and a comprehensive treatment plan, many people who suffer from clinical depression will get better. But, left untreated, episodes of depression may last a few months to several years, and they can be devastating, both for the people who experience them and for their families. People with severe depression can feel so hopeless that they become a risk for suicide.

An estimated 16 million American adults—almost 7% of the population—had at least one major depressive episode last year. People of all ages and all racial, ethnic, and socioeconomic backgrounds can experience depression, but the disorder does affect some groups of people more than others. Women are 70% more likely than men to experience depression, and young adults aged eighteen to twenty-five are 60% more likely to have depression than people aged fifty or older.

Getting a comprehensive evaluation and accurate diagnosis is important. A doctor needs to rule out any underlying medical issues or side effects of other medications (like beta blockers or antihypertensives) that can mimic a major depressive episode. To inform treatment options and shape a good treatment plan, it is important to understand life stressors, prior responses to treatment efforts, and any co-occurring conditions.

Symptoms

For most people, depression changes how they function day-to-day, though people with depression or experiencing a depressive episode have different symptoms.

- **Changes in sleep.** Many people have trouble falling asleep, staying asleep, or sleeping much longer than they used to. Waking up early in the morning is common for people with major depression.
- **Changes in appetite.** Depression can lead to serious weight loss or gain when a person stops eating or uses food as a coping mechanism.
- **Lack of concentration.** A person may be unable to focus during severe depression. Even reading the newspaper or following the plot of a TV show can be difficult. It becomes harder to make decisions, big or small.

- **Loss of energy.** People with depression may feel profound fatigue, think slowly, or be unable to perform normal daily routines.
- **Lack of interest.** People may lose interest in their usual activities or lose the capacity to experience pleasure. A person may have no desire to eat or have sex.
- **Low self-esteem.** During periods of depression, people dwell on losses or failures and feel excessive guilt and helplessness. Thoughts like "I am a loser" or "The world is a terrible place" or "I don't want to be alive" can take over.
- **Hopelessness.** Depression can make a person feel that nothing good will ever happen. Suicidal thoughts often follow these kinds of negative thoughts—and need to be taken seriously.
- **Changes in movement.** People with depression may look physically depleted or they may be agitated. For example, a person may wake early in the morning and pace the floor for hours.
- **Physical aches and pains.** Instead of talking about their emotions or sadness, some people may complain about a headache or an upset stomach.

People describe the symptoms of depression differently depending on the cultural lens they are looking through. In Western cultures, people generally talk about their moods or feelings, whereas in many Eastern cultures, people refer to physical pain.

Causes

Depression does not have a single cause. It can be triggered by a life crisis, physical illness, or another event, but may also occur spontaneously. Scientists believe several factors contribute to cause depression:

- **Trauma.** When people experience trauma at an early age, it can cause long-term changes in how their brains respond to fear and stress. These brain changes may explain why people who have a history of childhood trauma are more likely to experience depression.
- **Genetics.** Mood disorders and risk of suicide tend to run in families, but genetic inheritance is only one factor. Identical twins

share 100% of the same genes, but will both develop depression only about 30% of the time. People who have a genetic tendency to develop depression are more likely to show signs at a younger age. While a person may have a genetic tendency, life factors and events seem to influence whether he or she will ever actually experience an episode.

- **Life circumstances.** Marital status, financial standing, and where a person lives affect the incidence of depression, but this can be a case of "the chicken or the egg." For example, depression is more common in people who are homeless, but the depression itself may have caused the homelessness.

- **Brain structure.** Imaging studies have shown that the frontal lobe of the brain becomes less active when a person is depressed. Brain patterns during sleep change in a characteristic way. Depression is also associated with changes in how the pituitary gland and hypothalamus respond to hormone stimulation.

- **Other medical conditions.** People who have a history of sleep disturbances, medical illness, chronic pain, anxiety, and attention-deficit hyperactivity disorder (ADHD) are more likely to develop depression.

- **Drug and alcohol abuse.** Approximately 30% of people with substance abuse problems also have depression.

Who Gets Depression

Depression affects people of all ages and all racial, ethnic, and socioeconomic groups. But different groups of people do experience depression in different ways.

- **Children and teens.** All children experience ups and downs while growing up, but for some, the downs aren't commonplace—they are symptoms of depression. Children and teens at higher risk for depression include those who have attention deficit/hyperactivity disorder (ADHD), learning or anxiety disorders, and oppositional defiance disorder. A young person who has experienced considerable stress or trauma, faced a significant loss, or has a family history of mood disorders is at increased risk for depression.

Children with depression are more likely to complain of aches and pains than to say they are depressed. Teens with depression may become aggressive, engage in risky behavior, abuse drugs or alcohol, do poorly in school, or run away. Teens experiencing episodes of depression have an increased risk for suicide. In fact, suicide is the third-leading cause of death among children aged fifteen to nineteen.

- **Men.** For cultural reasons, men may feel more shame about their depression and simply try to tough it out or use alcohol or drugs to self-medicate. Untreated depression in men can have devastating consequences, as men are about four times more likely to die by suicide than women.

- **Women.** Many factors unique to women's lives play a role in whether they develop depression, including genetics, biology, reproduction, hormonal changes, and interpersonal relationships. During their menstrual cycles, many women experience behavioral and physical changes. These changes can include depressed feelings, irritability, and other emotional and physical changes. Many women with depression experience worsening symptoms before their periods. Women who have premenstrual syndrome (PMS) or premenstrual dysphoric disorder (PMDD) will experience gradually worsening symptoms until menstruation starts. Researchers are exploring how the cyclical change in hormones may affect the brain chemistry associated with depression.

  Many women experience a temporary mood disturbance after childbirth. But an estimated 9-16% of American women will experience postpartum depression, a disorder that occurs after pregnancy. Women with postpartum depression may find it difficult to function day-to-day because the illness can cause anxiety, insomnia, bouts of crying, and thoughts of hurting themselves or the child.

- **Seniors.** Depression in elderly people often goes untreated because many people think that depression is a normal part of aging and a natural reaction to chronic illness, loss, and social transition. Depression symptoms in older people may differ from younger people's symptoms. Depression in seniors can be characterized by memory problems, vague complaints of pain, and delusions. Depression can be a side effect of some medications commonly prescribed to older persons. For example, medications to treat hypertension and conditions such as heart attack, stroke, hip fracture, or macular degeneration are known to be associated with the development of depression.

- **LGBTQ.** Lesbian, gay, bisexual, transgender, and questioning (LGBTQ) people are at higher risk for depression because they regularly face discrimination from society at large and sometimes from family members, coworkers, or classmates. The stigma experienced by some LGBTQ people can make them more vulnerable to mental health conditions including depression.

Diagnosis

To be diagnosed with depression, a person must have experienced a major depressive episode that has lasted longer than two weeks. The symptoms of a major depressive episode include:

- Loss of interest or loss of pleasure in all activities.
- Change in appetite or weight.
- Sleep disturbances.
- Feeling agitated or feeling slowed down.
- Fatigue.
- Feelings of low self-worth, guilt or shortcomings.
- Difficulty concentrating or making decisions.
- Suicidal thoughts or intentions.

Diagnosing depression can be complicated because a depressive episode can be part of bipolar disorder or another mental illness. How a person describes symptoms often depends on the cultural lens through which life is viewed. Research has shown that African Americans and Latinos are more likely to be misdiagnosed, so people who have been diagnosed with depression should look for a health care professional who understands their background and shares their expectations for treatment.

Related Conditions

A person with depression may have additional conditions:

- Anxiety disorders, including posttraumatic stress disorder (PTSD).
- Attention-deficit hyperactivity disorder (ADHD).
- Substance abuse.

These conditions can make it hard to treat depression, but successfully treating depression almost always improves these related illnesses. Successful treatment of PTSD, ADHD, or substance abuse usually also improves the symptoms of depression.

Treatment

Although depression can be a devastating illness, it often responds to treatment. The key is to get a specific evaluation and a treatment plan. Today, a variety of treatment options are available for people with depression.

- Medications including antidepressants, mood stabilizers, and antipsychotic medications.
- Psychotherapy including cognitive behavioral therapy, family-focused therapy, and interpersonal therapy.
- Brain stimulation therapies including electroconvulsive therapy (ECT) or repetitive transcranial magnetic stimulation (rTMS).
- Light therapy, which uses a light box to expose a person to full spectrum light and regulate the hormone melatonin.
- Exercise.
- Alternative therapies including acupuncture, meditation, and nutrition.
- Self-management strategies and education.
- Mind/body/spirit approaches such as meditation, faith, and prayer.

Though depression cannot be cured, it can be treated effectively.

DISRUPTIVE MOOD DYSREGULATION DISORDER

A new diagnosis, Disruptive Mood Dysregulation Disorder (DMDD), was added to the *Diagnostic and Statistical Manual of Mental Disorders* (DSM) in 2014. As a relatively new diagnosis, there is still research being done to understand the disorder and to find effective treatment options.

Symptoms

DMDD is characterized by chronic irritability, anger or outbursts that are out of proportion to the situation that prompts them and inappropriate to the developmental milestones of the child. It may involve severe verbal or behavioral outbursts that occur 3 or more times a week and significantly impair the child's ability to function in daily activities in numerous settings.

One of the criteria of DMDD is that the symptoms cannot be explained by another mental illness (i.e. bipolar disorder, or oppositional defiance disorder) or by another medical or neurological cause.

To be diagnosed with DMDD, a child must have these symptoms steadily for 12 or more months. It is also not currently diagnosed under the age of 6 and over the age of 18.

Causes

There are currently no specific identified causes of DMDD although research has suggested several possible connections:

- **Environmental links.** While the genetic link seems very low (there is a low correlation between parents who exhibited DMDD symptoms and children who are diagnosed), life factors and events seem to influence whether a child develops DMDD. Family problems or conflict, divorce, moves or death may be culprits in triggering DMDD; abuse or psychological trauma is a possible cause, or alcohol or drug use during pregnancy may increase risk.
- **Poor general health.** Some research has suggested that poor diet - particularly deficiencies of B12, folate or iron – may contribute to DMDD, or that neurological problems like migraines may trigger DMDD.

Treatment

As a new diagnosis, treatment options are still being explored and the best treatments for DMDD are currently those also used to treat symptoms of anger or irritability in other mental illnesses. These options include:

- Medications including antidepressants, stimulants, and atypical antipsychotic medications.
- Psychotherapy including cognitive behavioral therapy, family-focused therapy (including parent training), and computer-based training.

DISSOCIATIVE DISORDERS

Dissociative disorders are considered to be an involuntary escape from reality characterized by a disconnection between thoughts, identity, consciousness, and memory. People from all age groups and racial, ethnic, and socioeconomic backgrounds can experience a dissociative disorder.

It's estimated that 2% of people experience dissociative disorders, with women being more likely than men to be diagnosed. Almost half of adults in the United States experience at least one depersonalization/derealization episode in their lives but only 2% meeting the full criteria for chronic episodes that characterize the disorder.

The symptoms of a dissociative disorder usually first develop as a response to a traumatic event, such as abuse or military combat, to keep those memories under control. Stressful situations can worsen symptoms and cause problems with functioning in everyday activities. However, the symptoms a person experiences will depend on the type of dissociative disorder that a person has.

Treatment for dissociative disorders often involves psychotherapy and medication. Though finding an effective treatment plan can be difficult, many people are able to live healthy and productive lives.

Symptoms

Symptoms and signs of dissociative disorders include:

- Significant memory loss of specific times, people, and events.
- Out-of-body experiences, such as feeling as though you are watching a movie of yourself.
- Mental health problems such as depression, anxiety, and thoughts of suicide.
- A sense of detachment from your emotions, or emotional numbness.
- A lack of a sense of self-identity.

The symptoms of dissociative disorders depend on the type of disorder that has been diagnosed. The *Diagnostic and Statistical Manual of Mental Disorders* (DSM) defines three types of dissociative disorders:

- **Dissociative amnesia.** The main symptom is difficulty remembering important information about one's self. Dissociative amnesia may surround a particular event, such as combat or abuse, or more rarely, information about identity and life history. The onset for an amnesic episode is usually sudden, and an episode can last minutes, hours, days, or, rarely, months or years. There is no average age of onset, and a person may experience multiple episodes throughout life.
- **Depersonalization disorder.** This disorder involves ongoing feelings of detachment. In depersonalization, a person feels detached from actions, feelings, thoughts, and sensations, as if watching a movie. In derealization, other people and things in the world around them seem unreal. In depersonalization disorder, a person may experience depersonalization, derealization, or both. Symptoms can last just a matter of moments or return at times over the years. The average onset age is sixteen, although depersonalization episodes can start in early or mid-childhood. Less than 20% of people with this disorder start experiencing episodes after the age of twenty.
- **Dissociative identity disorder (DID).** Formerly known as multiple personality disorder, this disorder is characterized by alternating between multiple identities. People with this disorder

may feel like one or more voices in their heads are trying to take control. Often, these identities may have unique names, characteristics, mannerisms, and voices. People with DID experience gaps in memory of everyday events, personal information, and trauma. Onset for the full disorder can happen at any age, but it is more likely to occur in people who have experienced severe, ongoing trauma before the age of five. Women are more likely to be diagnosed, as they more frequently present with acute dissociative symptoms. Men are more likely to deny symptoms and trauma histories, and commonly exhibit more violent behavior, rather than amnesia or fugue (confused or dissociative) states. This can lead to elevated false negative diagnosis.

Causes

Dissociative disorders usually develop as a way of dealing with trauma, and most often form in children exposed to long-term physical, sexual, or emotional abuse. Natural disasters and combat can also cause dissociative disorders.

Diagnosis

Doctors diagnose dissociative disorders based on a review of symptoms and personal history. A doctor may perform tests to rule out physical conditions (such as head injury, brain lesions or tumors, sleep deprivation, or intoxication), which can cause symptoms such as memory loss and a sense of unreality. After physical causes are ruled out, a mental health specialist is often consulted to conduct an evaluation.

Many features of dissociative disorders can be influenced by a person's cultural background. In the case of dissociative identity disorder and dissociative amnesia, patients may present with unexplained, non-epileptic seizures, paralyses, or sensory losses. In settings where spirit possession is part of cultural beliefs, the fragmented identities of a person who has DID may take the form of spirits, deities, demons, or animals. Intercultural contact may also influence the characteristics of other identities. For example, a person in India exposed to Western culture may present with an "alter" who only speaks English. In cultures with highly restrictive social conditions, amnesia is frequently triggered by severe psychological stress such as conflict caused by oppression. Finally, voluntarily induced states of depersonalization can be a part of meditative practices prevalent in many religions and cultures, and should not be diagnosed as a disorder.

Related Conditions

Because dissociative disorders appear on the trauma spectrum, many patients may have conditions associated with trauma, as well as additional trauma-based conditions.

- Posttraumatic stress disorder (PTSD).
- Borderline personality disorder (BPD).
- Substance abuse.
- Depression.
- Anxiety.

Treatment

Dissociative disorders are managed through various therapies including:

- Psychotherapies such as cognitive behavioral therapy (CBT) and dialectical behavioral therapy (DBT).
- Eye movement desensitization and reprocessing (EMDR).
- Medications such as antidepressants to treat symptoms of related conditions.

EATING DISORDERS

When a person becomes so preoccupied with food and weight issues that they find it hard to focus on other aspects of life, it may be an early sign of an eating disorder. Eating disorders are a serious mental illness and disease that can be easily overlooked but, without treatment, these disorders can ultimately take over a person's life and lead to serious, potentially fatal medical complications. Although eating disorders are commonly associated with women, men can develop them as well. Consider:

- 1 in 20 people will be affected at some point.
- 81% of 10-year-olds are afraid of being fat.
- 42% of first- through third-grade girls want to be thinner.
- Up to 8% of the U.S. population (nearly 24 million people) suffers from an eating disorder.
- 95% of those who have eating disorders are between the ages of 12 and 25.
- An estimated 10-15% of people with anorexia or bulimia are male.
- Only 1 in 10 with eating disorders receives treatment.
- Eating disorder research is extremely underfunded.

Symptoms

Eating disorders are a group of related conditions that cause serious emotional and physical problems. All of these conditions involve extreme food and weight issues, though each one has unique symptoms that separate it from the others.

- **Anorexia Nervosa.** Obsessing about weight loss, a person with anorexia will deny hunger and refuse to eat to the point of self-starvation. While some patients only restrict their eating, others may practice binge-eating and purging behaviors or exercise to the point of exhaustion in an attempt to limit, eliminate, or "burn" calories. Anorexics often develop food rituals or eliminate whole categories of food from their diet out of fear of being "fat."

The emotional symptoms of anorexia include irritability, social withdrawal, lack of mood or emotion, inability to understand the seriousness of the situation, fear of eating in public, and obsessions with food and exercise. Anorexia can also take a heavy physical toll. Very low food intake and inadequate nutrition causes a person to become very thin. The body is forced to slow down to conserve energy, causing irregularities or loss of menstruation, constipation and abdominal pain, irregular heart rhythms, low blood pressure, dehydration, and trouble sleeping.

- **Bulimia Nervosa.** Someone living with bulimia will feel out of control when binging on very large amounts of food during short periods of time, and then desperately try to eliminate the extra calories by forcing vomiting, abusing laxatives, or exercising excessively. This becomes a repeating cycle that controls many aspects of the person's life and has a very negative effect both emotionally and physically.

  People living with bulimia are usually normal weight or even a bit overweight. The emotional symptoms of bulimia include low self-esteem linked to body image, feelings of being out of control, feeling guilty or shameful about eating, and withdrawal from friends and family. Like anorexia, bulimia inflicts physical damage. The binging and purging can severely harm the parts of the body involved in eating and digesting food, teeth are damaged by frequent vomiting, and acid reflux is common. Excessive purging can cause dehydration that affects the body's electrolytes and can lead to cardiac arrhythmias, heart failure, and even death.

- **Binge Eating Disorder (BED).** Losing control over eating, a person with BED eats a very large amount of food in a short period of time, when not hungry, or even when uncomfortably full. This causes the person to feel embarrassed, disgusted, depressed, or guilty about the behavior. Unlike someone with anorexia or bulimia, the person with BED does not attempt to purge or exercise excessively after a binge-eating episode. People with BED may be of normal weight, overweight, or obese.

Causes

Eating disorders are very complex conditions, and scientists are still learning about the causes, which are varied and, often, attributed to a combination of factors. Although eating disorders all have food and weight issues in common, most experts now believe that eating disorders are caused by people attempting to cope with overwhelming feelings and painful emotions by controlling food. Unfortunately, this will eventually damage a person's sense of control as well as their physical and emotional health and self-esteem. Factors that may be involved in developing an eating disorder include:

- **Genetics.** People with first-degree relatives, siblings, or parents who have an eating disorder appear to be more at risk of developing an eating disorder, too. According to the Eating Disorder Coalition, the risk of developing an eating disorder is 50-80% genetics. This strongly suggests a genetic link and, in fact, researchers from the University of Iowa and the University of Texas Southwestern Medical Center have identified two gene mutations, ESSRA and HDAS4, that increase the risk of eating disorders. As further evidence of genetic and biological factors, an imbalance of the brain chemical serotonin is involved in contributing to eating disorders.

- **Environmental Factors.** Cultural pressures that praise "thinness" as beautiful for women and muscular development and body size as desirable for men place undue pressure on people to achieve unrealistic standards. Popular culture and media images often tie thinness to popularity, success, beauty, and happiness. This creates a strong desire to be very thin. Participating in professions and careers that promote thinness and weight loss (i.e. ballet and modeling) can contribute, as can involvement in aesthetic and weight-oriented sports such as diving, gymnastics, and wrestling.

- **Peer Pressure.** With young people, this can be a powerful force. Pressure can manifest in the form of teasing, bullying, or ridicule about size, weight or body image, and social pressures that value people on their physical appearance rather than inner-qualities can also have an effect. A history of physical or sexual abuse can also contribute to some people developing an eating disorder.

- **Emotional Health or Psychological Factors.** Perfectionism, impulsive behavior, and difficult relationships can all contribute to lowering a person's self-esteem and making them vulnerable to developing eating disorders, as can low self-esteem, depression, anxiety, stress, feelings of inadequacy, or lack of feeling in control in life.

Eating disorders affect all types of people. However, certain risk factors put some people at greater risk for developing an eating disorder.

- **Age.** Eating disorders are much more common during teens and early twenties.
- **Gender.** Statistically, teenage girls and young women are more likely to have eating disorders, but they are also more likely to be noticed and treated. Teenage boys and men are less likely to seek help, but studies show that one out of ten people diagnosed with eating disorders are male.
- **Family history.** Having a parent or sibling with an eating disorder increases the risk.
- **Dieting.** Dieting taken too far can become an eating disorder.
- **Changes.** Times of change—like going to college, starting a new job, or getting divorced—may be a stressor toward developing an eating disorder.
- **Vocations and activities.** Eating disorders are especially common among gymnasts, runners, wrestlers, and dancers.

Diagnosis

A person with an eating disorder will have the best recovery outcome if he or she is diagnosed early. These are some signs that indicate that someone may be struggling with an eating disorder:

- They have guilt and shame about eating.
- They have low self-esteem.
- They have a compulsive need for body perfection.
- They are extremely concerned about appearance.
- They are constantly occupied with food and/or weight.
- They significantly reduce eating and/or have a significant weight loss.
- There is evidence of purging (vomiting, diuretic abuse, excessive exercise).

If an eating disorder is suspected, a doctor will usually perform a physical examination, conduct an interview, and order lab tests to help to form the diagnosis and to check for related medical issues and complications. In addition, a mental health professional will conduct a psychological evaluation, asking questions about eating habits, behaviors, and beliefs. This might also include questions about a history of dieting, exercise, and bingeing and purging.

To warrant a diagnosis, symptoms must meet the criteria in the *Diagnostic and Statistical Manual of Mental Disorders* (DSM). Each eating disorder has its own diagnostic criteria that a mental health professional will use to determine which disorder is involved. It is not necessary to have all the criteria for a disorder to benefit from working with a mental health professional on food and eating issues.

How Do I Approach Someone I Think Has an Eating Disorder?

Since an eating disorder is a coping mechanism for other issues that the person doesn't know how to confront in a healthy way, focus the conversation on how the person is doing emotionally, rather than on their eating. With so much shame and fear associated with having an eating disorder, this is tricky. Here are some tips to try:

▶ Acknowledge that you've noticed something: "You seem really stressed and upset lately. I'm worried about you. What's going on?"
▶ Use empathy: "I know you have a stressful schedule and a lot of after school activities. I would really struggle with all that you've got going on. How is it affecting you?"
▶ Be compassionate and listen without judging. Validate the feelings you hear, rather than saying what to feel.
▶ Encourage getting help.
▶ Don't be surprised if you are shut down on your first attempt to talk.

Often, a person with an eating disorder will have symptoms of another mental health condition that requires treatment. Whenever possible, it is best to identify and address all conditions at the same time to provide comprehensive treatment support that helps to insure a lasting recovery.

Related Conditions

People with eating disorders often have additional illnesses:

* Depression.
* Anxiety disorders.

- Borderline personality disorder.
- Obsessive-compulsive disorder.
- Substance abuse.

Treating these illnesses can help make it easier to treat an eating disorder. Some of the symptoms of eating disorders may be caused by other illnesses.

Treatment

Eating disorders are managed using a variety of techniques, which vary depending on the type of disorder. Treatments generally include the following:

- Nutritional counseling and weight restoration monitoring are crucial. Family-based treatment is especially important for families with children and adolescents because it enlists the families' help to better insure healthy eating patterns and increases awareness and support.
- Psychotherapy, such as talk therapy or behavioral therapy.
- Medicine, such as antidepressants and anti-anxiety drugs that can help reduce the impact of underlying issues.

OBSESSIVE-COMPULSIVE DISORDER

Obsessive-compulsive disorder (OCD) is characterized by repetitive, unwanted, intrusive thoughts (obsessions) and irrational, excessive urges to do certain actions (compulsions). Although people with OCD may know that their thoughts and behavior don't make sense, they are often unable to stop them.

Symptoms typically begin during childhood, the teenage years, or young adulthood, although males often develop them at a younger age than females. More than 2% of the U.S. population (nearly one out of forty people) will be diagnosed with OCD during their lives.

Symptoms

Most people have occasional obsessive thoughts or compulsive behaviors. In an obsessive-compulsive disorder, however, these symptoms generally last more than an hour each day and interfere with daily life.

Obsessions are intrusive, irrational thoughts or impulses that repeatedly occur. People with these disorders know these thoughts are irrational but are afraid that somehow they might be true. These thoughts and impulses are upsetting, and people may try to ignore or suppress them.

Examples of obsessions include:

- Thoughts about harming or having harmed someone.
- Doubts about having done something right, like turning off the stove or locking a door.
- Unpleasant sexual images.
- Fears of saying or shouting inappropriate things in public.

Compulsions are repetitive acts that temporarily relieve the stress brought on by an obsession. People with these disorders know that these rituals don't make sense but feel they must perform them to relieve the anxiety and, in some cases, to prevent something bad from happening. Like obsessions, people may try not to perform compulsive acts but feel forced to do so to relieve anxiety.

Examples of compulsions include:

- Handwashing due to a fear of germs.
- Counting and recounting money because the person can't be sure they added correctly.
- Checking to see if a door is locked or the stove is off.
- "Mental checking" that goes with intrusive thoughts is also a form of compulsion.

Causes

The exact cause of obsessive-compulsive disorders is unknown, but researchers believe that activity in several portions of the brain is responsible. More specifically, these areas of the brain may not respond normally to serotonin, a chemical that some nerve cells use to communicate with each other. Genetics are thought to be very important. If you, your parent, or a sibling, have an obsessive-compulsive disorder, chances are nearly 25% that another immediate family member will have it.

Diagnosis

A general physical with blood tests is recommended to make sure symptoms are not caused by drug abuse, medications, another mental illness, or by a general medical condition. The sudden appearance of symptoms in children or older people merits a thorough medical evaluation to ensure that another illness is not causing of these symptoms.

To be diagnosed with OCD, a person must have:

- Obsessions, compulsions, or both.
- Obsessions or compulsions that are upsetting, typically last for at least an hour each day, and cause difficulty with work, relationships, or other parts of life.

Related Conditions

Some other conditions share characteristics with OCD but are considered separate conditions.

- **Body Dysmorphic Disorder.** This disorder is characterized by an obsession with physical appearance. Unlike simple vanity, BDD is characterized by obsessing over one's appearance and body image, often for many hours a day. Any perceived flaws cause significant distress and ultimately impede on the person's ability to function. In extreme cases, BDD can lead to bodily injury due to excessive exercise, unnecessary surgical procedures to change one's appearance, or due to infection resulting from skin picking.

- **Hoarding Disorder.** This disorder is defined by the drive to collect a large amount of useless or valueless items, coupled with extreme distress at the idea of throwing anything away. Over time, this situation can render a space unhealthy or dangerous to be in. Hoarding disorder can negatively impact someone emotionally, physically, socially, and financially, and often leads to distress and disability. In addition, many hoarders cannot see that their actions are potentially harmful so they may resist diagnosis or treatment.
- **Trichotillomania.** Many people develop unhealthy habits such as nail biting or teeth grinding, especially during periods of high stress. Trichotillomania, however, is the compulsive urge to pull out (and possibly eat) your own hair, including eyelashes and eyebrows. Some people may consciously pull out their hair, while others may not even be aware that they are doing it. Trichotillomania can create serious injuries, such as repetitive motion injury in the arm or hand, or, if the hair is repeatedly swallowed, the formation of hairballs in the stomach, which can be life-threatening if left untreated. A similar illness is excoriation disorder, which is the compulsive urge to scratch or pick at the skin.

Treatment

Though OCD cannot be cured, it can be treated effectively. Typical treatment plans often include both psychotherapy and medications, and combined treatment is usually optimal.

- **Medication**, especially a type of antidepressant called a selective serotonin reuptake inhibitor (SSRI), is helpful for many people to reduce obsessions and compulsions.
- **Psychotherapy** is also helpful in relieving obsessions and compulsions. In particular, cognitive behavior therapy (CBT) and exposure and response therapy (ERT) are effective for many people. Exposure response prevention therapy helps a person tolerate the anxiety associated with obsessive thoughts while not acting out a compulsion to reduce that anxiety. Over time, this leads to less anxiety and more self-mastery.

POSTTRAUMATIC STRESS DISORDER

In a physical crisis or traumatic event—such as military combat, an assault, accident, or a natural disaster—the human body focuses all its resources and energy on getting out of harm's way. The heart rate increases to pump blood to muscles for movement and preparing to fight or flee. These instincts can be life-saving during a crisis. But sometimes this reaction can have long-lasting negative effects when our biological responses leave people with ongoing psychological symptoms because they are not integrated into consciousness. The resulting damage to the brain's response system is called posttraumatic stress response or disorder, also known as PTSD.

PTSD affects 3.5% of the U.S. adult population—about 7.7 million Americans—but women are more likely to develop the condition than men. About 37% of those cases are classified as severe. While PTSD can occur at any age, the average age of onset is in a person's early twenties.

Symptoms

The symptoms of PTSD fall into the following categories:

- **Intrusive Memories**, which can include flashbacks of reliving the moment of trauma, bad dreams, and scary thoughts.
- **Avoidance**, which can include staying away from certain places or objects that are reminders of the traumatic event. A person may also feel numb, guilty, worried, or depressed or have trouble remembering the traumatic event.
- **Dissociation**, which can include out-of-body experiences or de-realization, which is a feeling that the world is "not real."
- **Hypervigilance**, which can include being startled very easily, feeling tense, having trouble sleeping, or experiencing outbursts of anger.

Over the last five years, research on children from one to six years old found that young children can develop PTSD, and the symptoms are quite different from those of adults. These findings also saw an increase in PTSD diagnoses in young children by more than eight times when using the newer criteria. Symptoms in young children can include:

- Acting out scary events during playtime.
- Forgetting how to talk or being unable to talk.
- Being excessively clingy with adults.
- Extreme temper tantrums, as well as overly aggressive behavior.

Diagnosis

Symptoms of PTSD usually begin within three months after a traumatic event, but occasionally emerge years afterward. Symptoms must last more than a month to be considered PTSD. PTSD is often accompanied by depression, substance abuse, or another anxiety disorder.

People describe symptoms in a variety of ways, often depending on their cultural lens. In Western cultures, people generally talk about their moods or feelings, while in many Eastern cultures, people more commonly refer to physical pain. African Americans and Latinos are more likely to be misdiagnosed, so they should look for a health care professional who understands their background and shares their expectations for treatment.

In order to detect PTSD in preschool children, research indicates that diagnostic criteria need to be more behaviorally anchored and developmentally sensitive since young children have emerging abstract cognitive abilities and limited verbal expression. The National Center for PTSD has more information on the preschool subtype.

Related Conditions

In addition to thoughts of or attempts at suicide, someone with PTSD may also have additional disorders:

- Anxiety disorders, including Generalized Anxiety Disorder.
- OCD.
- Borderline Personality Disorder.

- Depression.
- Substance abuse.

These other illnesses can make it challenging to treat PTSD. For example, medications used to treat OCD or depression may worsen symptoms of PTSD, and may even trigger them. However, successfully treating PTSD almost always improves these related illnesses and successful treatment of depression, other anxiety disorders, or substance abuse usually improves the symptoms of PTSD.

Treatment

Though PTSD cannot be cured, it can be treated and managed effectively with several tools:

- Medications, including mood stabilizers, antipsychotic medications, and antidepressants.
- Psychotherapy, such as cognitive behavioral therapy or group therapy.
- Self-management strategies, such as "self-soothing." Many therapy techniques, including mindfulness, are helpful to ground a person and bring her back to reality after a dissociative episode or a flashback.
- Service animals, especially dogs, can help soothe some of the symptoms of PTSD.

SCHIZOAFFECTIVE DISORDER

Schizoaffective disorder is a chronic mental health condition characterized primarily by symptoms of schizophrenia—such as hallucinations or delusions—and symptoms of a mood disorder—such as mania and depression. There are two major types of schizoaffective disorder: **bipolar** type and **depressive** type.

Since schizoaffective disorder shares symptoms of multiple mental health conditions, many people who have this disorder are incorrectly diagnosed at first with bipolar disorder or schizophrenia. Less well-studied than schizophrenia and bipolar disorder, schizoaffective disorder borrows many interventions, resources, and treatment approaches from those disorders.

Schizoaffective disorder is seen in about 0.3% of the population. Men and women experience this disorder at the same rate, but men often develop the illness at an earlier age. Schizoaffective disorder can be managed effectively with medication and therapy, but co-occurring substance abuse disorders are a serious risk and require integrated treatment.

Symptoms

The symptoms of schizoaffective disorder can be severe and need to be monitored closely. Depending on the type of mood disorder diagnosed—depression or bipolar disorder—people will experience different symptoms:

- **Hallucinations** (seeing or hearing things that aren't there).
- **Delusions** (false, fixed beliefs that are held regardless of contradictory evidence).
- **Disorganized thinking.** A person may switch very quickly from one topic to another or provide answers that are completely unrelated to questions they are asked.
- **Depressed mood.** If a person has been diagnosed with schizoaffective disorder depressive type, they will experience feelings of sadness, emptiness, feeling of worthlessness, or other symptoms of depression.
- **Manic behavior.** If a person has been diagnosed with schizoaffective disorder: bipolar type, they will experience feelings of euphoria, racing thoughts, increased risky behavior, and other symptoms of mania.

Causes

The exact cause of schizoaffective disorder is unknown. A combination of causes may contribute to the development of schizoaffective disorder.

- **Genetics.** Schizoaffective disorder tends to run in families. This does not mean that if a relative has an illness, you will absolutely get it but it does mean that there is a greater chance of family members developing the illness.
- **Brain chemistry and structure.** Science is only beginning to understand the ways in which brain function and structure may be different, but brain scans are helping to advance research in this area.
- **Stress.** Stressful events such as a death in the family, end of a marriage, or loss of a job can trigger symptoms or the onset of illness.
- **Drug use.** Psychoactive drugs such as LSD have been linked to the development of schizoaffective disorder.

Diagnosis

Schizoaffective disorder can be difficult to diagnose because it has symptoms of both schizophrenia and either depression or bipolar disorder. To be diagnosed with schizoaffective disorder a person must have the following symptoms:

- A period during which there is a major mood disorder, either depression or mania, that occurs at the same time that symptoms of schizophrenia are present.
- Delusions or hallucinations for two or more weeks in the absence of a major mood episode.
- Symptoms that meet criteria for a major mood episode are present for the majority of the total duration of the illness.
- The abuse of drugs or medication is not responsible for the symptoms.

Related Conditions

A person with schizoaffective disorder may have additional illnesses:

- Anxiety disorder.
- Posttraumatic stress disorder (PTSD).
- Attention-deficit hyperactivity disorder (ADHD).

- Substance abuse.

Treatment

Schizoaffective disorder is treated and managed in several ways:

- Medications, including mood stabilizers, antipsychotic medications and antidepressants.
- Psychotherapy, such as cognitive behavioral therapy or family-focused therapy.
- Self-management strategies and education.

SCHIZOPHRENIA

Schizophrenia is a serious mental illness that interferes with a person's ability to think clearly, manage emotions, make decisions, and relate to others. It is a complex, long-term medical illness, affecting about 1% of Americans. Although schizophrenia can occur at any age, the average age of onset tends to be in the late teens to the early twenties for men, and the late twenties to early thirties for women. It is uncommon for schizophrenia to be diagnosed in a person younger than twelve or older than forty. It is possible to live well with schizophrenia.

Symptoms

It can be difficult to diagnose schizophrenia in teens because the first signs can include a change of friends, a drop in grades, sleep problems, and irritability—common and nonspecific adolescent behavior. Other factors include isolating oneself and withdrawing from others, an increase in unusual thoughts and suspicions, and a family history of psychosis. In young people who develop schizophrenia, this stage of the disorder is called the "prodromal" period.

With any condition, it's essential to get a comprehensive medical evaluation in order to obtain the best diagnosis. For a diagnosis of schizophrenia, some of the following symptoms are present in the context of reduced functioning for a least six months:

- **Hallucinations** include hearing voices, seeing things, or smelling things that others can't perceive. A hallucination is very real to the person experiencing it, and it may be very confusing for a loved one to witness. The voices in the hallucination can be critical or threatening. Voices may involve people who are known or unknown to the person hearing them.
- **Delusions** are false beliefs that don't change even when the person who holds them is presented with new ideas or facts. People who have delusions often also have problems concentrating, confused thinking, or the sense that their thoughts are blocked.
- **Negative symptoms** are ones that diminish a person's abilities. Negative symptoms often include being emotionally flat or speaking in a dull, disconnected way. People with negative symptoms may be unable to start or follow through with activities, show little interest in life, or may be unable to sustain relationships. Negative symptoms are sometimes confused with clinical depression.
- **Cognitive issues/disorganized thinking.** People with the cognitive symptoms of schizophrenia often struggle to remember things, organize their thoughts, or complete tasks. Commonly, people with schizophrenia have anosognosia or "lack of insight." This means the person is unaware that they have the illness, which can make treating or working with them much more challenging.

Causes

Research suggests that schizophrenia may have several possible causes:

- **Genetics.** Schizophrenia isn't caused by just one genetic variation, but a complex interplay of genetics and environmental influences. While schizophrenia occurs in 1% of the general population, having a history of family psychosis greatly increases the risk. Schizophrenia occurs in roughly 10% of people who have a first-degree relative with the disorder, such as a parent or sibling. The highest risk occurs in identical twins; when one is diagnosed with schizophrenia, the other has a roughly 50% chance of developing the disorder.

- **Environment.** Exposure to viruses or malnutrition before birth, particularly in the first and second trimesters, has been shown to increase the risk of schizophrenia. Inflammation or autoimmune diseases can also lead to increased compromise of the fetal immune system during pregnancy.

- **Brain chemistry.** Problems with certain brain chemicals, including the neurotransmitters dopamine and glutamate, may contribute to schizophrenia. Neurotransmitters allow brain cells to communicate with each other. Networks of neurons are likely involved as well.

- **Substance abuse.** Some studies have suggested that taking mind-altering drugs during teen years and young adulthood can increase the risk of schizophrenia. A growing body of evidence indicates that smoking marijuana increases the risk of psychotic incidents and the risk of ongoing psychotic experiences. The younger and more frequent the use, the greater the risk. Another study has found that smoking marijuana led to earlier onset of schizophrenia and often preceded the manifestation of the illness.

Diagnosis

Diagnosing schizophrenia is not easy. Sometimes, using drugs such as methamphetamines or LSD can cause a person to have schizophrenia-like symptoms. The difficulty of diagnosing this illness is compounded by the fact that many people who are diagnosed lack awareness or do not believe they have the disorder. These common symptoms of schizophrenia greatly complicate diagnosis and treatment.

While there is no single physical or lab test that can diagnose schizophrenia, a health care provider who evaluates the symptoms and the course of a person's illness over six months can help ensure a correct diagnosis. The health care provider must rule out other factors such as brain tumors, other physical conditions, and other psychiatric diagnoses, such as bipolar disorder.

To be diagnosed with schizophrenia, a person must have two or more of the following symptoms occurring persistently in the context of reduced functioning:

- Delusions.
- Hallucinations.
- Disorganized speech.
- Disorganized or catatonic behavior.
- Negative symptoms.

Delusions or hallucinations alone can often be enough to lead to a diagnosis of schizophrenia. Identifying it as early as possible greatly improves a person's chances of managing the illness, reducing psychotic episodes, and recovering. People who receive good care during their first psychotic episode are admitted to the hospital less often, and may require less time to control symptoms than those who don't receive immediate help. The literature on the role of medicines early in treatment is evolving, but we do know that psychotherapy is essential.

People describe symptoms in a variety of ways, often depending on an individual's cultural lens. African Americans and Latinos are more likely to be misdiagnosed, probably due to differing cultural or religious beliefs or language barriers. Any person who has been diagnosed with schizophrenia should try to work with a health care professional who understands his or her cultural background and shares the same expectations for treatment.

Related Conditions

People with schizophrenia may have additional illnesses including:

- Substance abuse.
- Post-Traumatic stress disorder.
- Obsessive-compulsive disorder.
- Major depression.

Successfully treating schizophrenia almost always improves these related illnesses, and successful treatment of substance abuse, PTSD, or OCD usually improves the symptoms of schizophrenia.

Treatment

There is no cure for schizophrenia, but it can be treated and managed in several ways.

- Antipsychotic medications.
- Psychotherapy, such as cognitive behavioral therapy, assertive community treatment, and supportive therapy.
- Self-management strategies and education.

SENSORY PROCESSING DISORDER

Sensory Processing Disorder (SPD) is a neurological condition that causes difficulties in processing information that arrives in the brain via the five senses - hearing, tasting, smelling, touching, and seeing – and integrating that stimulus with appropriate motor or behavioral responses. It may also include challenges with movement or positional perception. Other common names for SPD are Sensory Integration Dysfunction or Neurosensory Dysfunction. It is not currently a recognized medical diagnosis, and may co-occur with autism or other mental illness diagnoses.

Symptoms

Symptoms for SPD will vary based on whether there is overstimulation or under stimulation of sensory signals, and will also vary in intensity. Symptoms are generally consistent across different environments or unaffected by typical behavior influences like whether the child is more tired than usual, or is hungry or in a difficult mood.

- **Under-stimulation (or under-responsiveness).** Children whose under-respond to sensory stimuli may show little or no reaction to sensations like loud noises, bright lights or feeling dizzy when spinning. They may appear to be "laid back" in their responses to certain high sensory situations, or may seek out extra sensory input like overactive play, places with lots of action, or loud environments.

- **Over-stimulation (or over-responsiveness).** When the brain becomes over-stimulated by sensory input, children will often actively avoid situations or places that provide too much sensory input for their comfort. They may show a strong reaction to a certain texture, a preference for quiet play away from other children, or a fear of loud noises.

General symptoms may include lack of coordination (i.e. bumping into things because of their difficulty with positional perception), a difficulty in engaging in conversation or play, or extreme or non-appropriate reaction to lights, sounds, or smells.

Causes

There is no identified cause for Sensory Processing Disorder but research shows several possible factors:

- **Genetics.** While there is no definitive genetic link for SPD, several studies that compared the rate of occurrence in twins or in close family members suggest that there may be a genetic component to SPD that may also be connected to abnormal brain activity or an impairment of the neural network in the brain.
- **Environment.** There are a number of possible environmental contributors to SPD. Prenatal exposure to drugs or alcohol may play a part in interrupting normal brain signal function. Traumatic brain injury can also cause a sensory dysfunction that will be related to the part of the brain affected by the injury.

Diagnosis

Sensory Processing Disorder is not currently a recognized medical diagnosis with widely accepted criteria for evaluation and, like many mental illnesses, the symptoms will exist on a spectrum. However, a baseline assessment is usually considered when the child's reactions to sensory input are disruptive to their normal behavior and developmental milestones, or to their daily functioning. Medical providers may also treat SPD symptoms as part of a related mental illness diagnosis. While many children may go through periods of reacting to certain external stimulation that they eventually become acclimated to, in SPD those adjustments take more focused efforts.

Related Conditions

People with Sensory Processing Disorder may have additional diagnoses including:

- Autism.
- Asperger's Syndrome.
- Other developmental disabilities.

Treatment

Treatment for SPD usually takes the form of sensory integration that helps the child learn appropriate responses and behaviors related to their specific needs. Through practiced sessions of exposure to the stimulus, the intent is to retrain the brain to respond differently, and more appropriately, to the sensory stimuli.

Chapter 3—Related Conditions

Almost always, mental illnesses co-occur with other mental illnesses, conditions, symptoms, and syndromes. When conditions come hand-in-hand, they are called "comorbid." The lines are often blurred among disorders and related conditions, so it helps to know about comorbidities that may also be in the mix.

And we must remember that mental illness is a serious brain disease that can be terminal. According to the Centers for Disease Control (CDC), more than 41,000 individuals take their own lives each year. They leave behind thousands of friends and family members to navigate the tragedy of their loss. Suicide is the tenth leading cause of death among adults in the U.S. and the third leading cause of death among people aged ten to twenty-four.

RISK OF SUICIDE

If you or someone you know is in an emergency, call The National Suicide Prevention Lifeline for free at 1-800-273-TALK (8255) or call 911 immediately.

Suicidal thoughts or behaviors are both damaging and dangerous and are therefore considered a psychiatric emergency. Someone experiencing these thoughts should seek immediate assistance from a health or mental health care provider. Having suicidal thoughts does not mean someone is weak or flawed.

Suicide is probably every parent's worst nightmare because life is truly fragile and, in the blink of an eye, we could lose everything. Unfortunately, with so much stigma, shame, and misinformation associated with mental illness—and discussion about it too often in hushed, negative tones—we do not give suicide the preventive attention it deserves. As a society dealing with mental illness, we have got to realize that lives are at stake!

Know the Warning Signs

Threats or comments about killing themselves. Also known as suicidal ideation, can begin with seemingly harmless thoughts like "I wish I wasn't here," but can become more overt and dangerous.

- Increased alcohol and drug use.
- Aggressive behavior.
- Social withdrawal from friends, family, and the community.
- Dramatic mood swings.
- Talking, writing, or thinking about death.
- Impulsive or reckless behavior.

Is There Imminent Danger?

- Any person exhibiting these behaviors should get care immediately:
- Putting their affairs in order and giving away their possessions.
- Saying goodbye to friends and family.
- Mood shifts from despair to calm.
- Planning, possibly by looking around to buy, steal, or borrow the tools they need to commit suicide, such as a firearm or prescription medication.

If you are unsure, a licensed mental health professional can help assess risk. Do not wait to get your child the help they need.

Risk Factors for Suicide

Research has found that about 90% of individuals who die by suicide experience mental illness. A number of other things may put a person at risk of suicide, including:

- A family history of suicide.
- Substance abuse. Drugs and alcohol can result in mental highs and lows that exacerbate suicidal thoughts.
- Intoxication. More than one in three people who die from suicide are found to be currently under the influence.
- Access to firearms.
- A serious or chronic medical illness.
- Gender. Although more women than men attempt suicide, men are four times more likely to die by suicide.
- A history of trauma or abuse.
- Prolonged stress.
- Isolation.
- Age. People under age twenty-four or above age sixty-five are at a higher risk for suicide.
- A recent tragedy or loss.
- Agitation and sleep deprivation.

Can Thoughts of Suicide Be Prevented?

First and foremost, always take seriously any talk about suicide. If you or someone you know is suffering from a mental illness, talk to someone you trust—a friend, partner, or clergy member - and encourage your child to do the same. Young people should tell a teacher, parent, or trusted adult if they are having thoughts of suicide. If they don't know how to talk to someone they know, the National Suicide Prevention Lifeline is free and open 24/7: 1-800-273-TALK (8255).

Mental health professionals are trained to help a person understand their feelings and can improve mental wellness and resiliency. Depending on their training, they can provide effective ways to help.

Psychotherapy, such as cognitive behavioral therapy and dialectical behavior therapy, can help a person with thoughts of suicide recognize unhealthy patterns of thinking and behavior, validate troubling feelings, and learn coping skills.

Medication can be used if necessary to treat underlying depression and anxiety and can lower a person's risk of self-harm. Depending on the person's mental health diagnosis, other medications can also be used to alleviate symptoms.

There is help and there is hope.

ANOSOGNOSIA

When someone rejects a diagnosis of mental illness, it's tempting to say that he's "in denial." But someone with acute mental illness may not be thinking clearly enough to consciously choose denial. They may instead be experiencing "lack of insight" or "lack of awareness." The formal medical term for this condition is anosognosia, from the Greek meaning "to not know a disease."

When we talk about anosognosia in mental illness, we mean that someone is unaware of their own mental health condition or that they can't perceive their condition accurately. Anosognosia is a common symptom of certain mental illnesses, and perhaps the most difficult to understand for those who have never experienced it.

Anosognosia is relative. Self-awareness can vary over time, allowing a person to acknowledge their illness at times and making such knowledge impossible at other times. When insight shifts back and forth over time, we might think people are denying their condition out of fear or stubbornness, but variations in awareness are typical of anosognosia.

What Causes Anosognosia?

We constantly update our mental image of ourselves. When we get a sunburn, we adjust our self-image and expect to look different in the mirror. When we learn a new skill, we add it to our self-image and feel more competent. But this updating process is complicated. It requires the brain's frontal lobe to organize new information, develop a revised narrative, and remember the new self-image.

Brain imaging studies have shown that this crucial area of the brain can be damaged by schizophrenia and bipolar disorder as well as by diseases like dementia. When the frontal lobe isn't operating at 100%, a person may lose—or partially lose—the ability to update his or her self-image.

Without an update, we're stuck with our old self-image from before the illness started. Since our perceptions feel accurate, we conclude that our loved ones are lying or making a mistake. If family and friends insist they're right, the person with an illness may get frustrated or angry, or begin to avoid them.

Anosognosia affects 50% of people with schizophrenia, and 40% of people with bipolar disorder. It can also accompany illnesses such as major depression with psychotic features. Treating these mental health conditions is much more complicated if lack of insight is one of the symptoms. People with anosognosia are placed at increased risk of homelessness or arrest. Learning to understand anosognosia and its risks can improve the odds of helping people with this difficult symptom.

Why Is Insight Important?

For a person with anosognosia, this inaccurate insight feels as real and convincing as other people's ability to perceive themselves. But these misperceptions cause conflicts with others and increased anxiety. Lack of insight also typically causes a person to avoid treatment. This makes it the most common reason for people to stop taking their medications. And as it is often combined with psychosis or mania, lack of insight can cause reckless or undesirable behavior.

DUAL DIAGNOSIS

Dual diagnosis is a term for the condition of someone who experiences a mental illness and a substance abuse problem simultaneously. Dual diagnosis is a very broad category. It can range from someone developing mild depression because of binge drinking, to someone's symptoms of bipolar disorder becoming more severe when that person abuses heroin during periods of mania.

Either substance abuse or mental illness can develop first. A person experiencing a mental health condition may turn to drugs and alcohol as a form of self-medication to improve the troubling mental health symptoms they experience. However, research shows that drugs and alcohol only make the symptoms of mental health conditions worse. Further, drugs affect a person's moods, thoughts, brain chemistry, and behavior, so substance abuse can also lead to mental health problems.

How Common is a Dual Diagnosis?

About a third of all people experiencing mental illnesses and about half of people living with severe mental illnesses also experience substance abuse. These statistics are mirrored in the substance abuse community, where about a third of all alcohol abusers and more than half of all drug abusers report experiencing a mental illness.

Men are more likely to develop a co-occurring disorder than women, and individuals of lower socioeconomic status, military veterans, and people with general medical illnesses also have a particularly high risk of dual diagnosis.

Symptoms

The defining characteristic of dual diagnosis is that a mental health issue occurs simultaneously with a substance abuse disorder. Because many combinations of disorders can occur, the symptoms of dual diagnosis vary widely. The symptoms of substance abuse may include:

- Withdrawal from friends and family.
- Sudden changes in behavior.
- Using substances under dangerous conditions.
- Engaging in risky behaviors when drunk or high.

- Loss of control over use of substances.
- Doing things you wouldn't normally do to maintain your habit.
- Developing tolerance and withdrawal symptoms.
- Feeling like you need the drug to be able to function.

Some standard alcohol and drug screening tools are used in mental health clinics to identify people at risk for drug and alcohol abuse.

The symptoms of mental health conditions also can vary greatly. Knowing the warnings signs, such as extreme mood changes, confused thinking or problems concentrating, avoiding friends and social activities, and thoughts of suicide, can help signal a reason to seek help.

How is a Dual Diagnosis Treated?

The most common method of treatment for dual diagnosis today is integrated intervention, in which a person receives care for both a specific mental illness and substance abuse. Because a dual diagnosis may occur in many ways, treatment will not be the same for everyone.

Detoxification

The first major hurdle that people with dual diagnosis will have to pass is detoxification. During **inpatient detoxification**, a person is monitored 24/7 by a trained medical staff for up to seven days. The staff may administer tapering amounts of the substance or its medical alternative in order to wean a person off and lessen the effects of withdrawal.

Outpatient detoxification is sometimes an option for those considered with low to moderate withdrawal symptoms, and that have a good social support network available during the withdrawal process. Medical and counseling support are still provided, but the person can still maintain a work schedule and family relationships.

Inpatient detoxification is generally more effective than outpatient for initial sobriety. This is because inpatient treatment provides a consistent environment and removes the person battling addiction from exposure to people and places associated with their habits of use.

Inpatient Rehabilitation

A person experiencing a serious mental illness and dangerous or dependent patterns of abuse may benefit most from an inpatient rehabilitation center that can provide concentrated medical and mental health care 24/7. Such treatment centers provide therapy, support, medication, and health services with the goal of treating each patient's addiction as well as its underlying causes.

Supportive Housing

Group homes or sober houses are another type of residential treatment center that is most helpful for people who are newly sober or trying to avoid relapse. These treatment centers allow for more freedom while still providing round-the-clock care.

Medications

Medication is a useful tool for treating a variety of mental illnesses. Depending on the mental health symptoms a person is experiencing, different mental health medications may play an important role in recovery.

Certain medications are also helpful for people experiencing substance abuse, as they can help ease withdrawal symptoms during the detoxification process or promote recovery. Often, these medications produce similar effects in the body as the addictive drugs with fewer side effects or decreasing dependency.

Psychotherapy

Psychotherapy is almost always a large part of an effective dual diagnosis treatment plan. Education on a person's illness and how their beliefs and behaviors influence their thoughts has been shown in countless studies to improve the symptoms of both mental illness and substance abuse.

Cognitive behavioral therapy (CBT) in particular is effective in helping people with dual diagnosis learn how to cope and to change ineffective patterns of thinking.

Self-help and Support Groups

Dealing with a dual diagnosis can feel challenging and isolating. Support groups allow members to share frustrations, successes, referrals for specialists, resources in the community, and tips on what works best when trying to recover. They also form friendships and provide encouragement to stay clean. Here are some groups that can offer support:

- **Double Trouble in Recovery** is a 12-step fellowship for people managing both a mental illness and substance abuse.
- **Alcoholics Anonymous** and **Narcotics Anonymous** are 12-step groups for people recovering from alcohol or drug addiction.
- **Smart Recovery** is a sobriety support group program for people with a variety of addictions.

LEARNING DISORDERS

Learning disorders often travel hand-in-hand with certain mental illnesses, or can also cause symptoms of depression or anxiety as a child struggles with "keeping up" in a class or learning setting. Teaching effective strategies for managing the learning disability can often reduce some of those elements of the mental illness as well.

- **Auditory Processing Disorder.** Auditory process disorder (APD), or central auditory processing disorder (CAPD) is diagnosed when a person's brain is not able to process auditory information in a way that conveys adequate meaning. The physical structures of their ears are normal, but the brain does not interpret sounds in a recognizable code. APD is thought to be more prevalent in males, but can occur in all genders.

- **Nonverbal Learning Disorder.** Those with nonverbal learning disorder have difficulty interpreting nonverbal communication signals, like facial expressions or body language. This can lead to poor social skills as nonverbal cues are not recognized, and can also include poor visual/spatial skills, leading to poor coordination skills that impacts handwriting, sports abilities or general lack of coordination.
- **Dyslexia Disorder.** Often called a reading disorder, dyslexia is characterized by poor reading skills due to a lack of ability in connecting speech sounds to written letters or words (a process called decoding). It is not a lack of intelligence, but can create challenges processing written information.
- **Math Disorder.** Also called **dyscalculia** or "**math dyslexia**," math disorder is the inability to process number-related concepts, lack number sense (i.e. relating "5" to "five," lack working memory (the ability to keep numbers in mind during multi-step equations), or have difficulty using symbols in certain numeric concepts.

PSYCHOSIS

An episode of psychosis is when a person has a break from reality. Psychotic episodes often involve seeing, hearing, and believing things that aren't real. Approximately three in one hundred people will experience an episode of psychosis during their lives. Although psychotic episodes can occur at any age, young adults are at an increased risk of experiencing such episodes because of hormonal changes that occur during puberty, affecting the brain. A psychotic episode can be the result of a mental or physical illness, substance use, trauma, or extreme stress. Psychosis is not an illness, but a symptom.

Symptoms

Symptoms of a psychotic episode can include incoherent speech and disorganized behavior, such as unpredictable anger, but psychosis typically involves either hallucinations or delusions.

Hallucinations are seeing, hearing, or physically feeling things that aren't actually there. These might include:

- Voices telling you to commit acts of violence or self-harm.
- Feeling like something is crawling under your skin.
- Seeing someone take the shape of something they are not, such as a demon.

Delusions are strong beliefs that are unlikely to be true and may seem irrational to others. These might include:

- Believing external forces are controlling your thoughts, feelings, and behaviors.
- Believing that trivial remarks, events, or objects have personal meaning or significance.
- Thinking that you have special powers, are on a special mission, or even that you are God.

Early Warning Signs

Most people think of psychosis as a sudden break from reality, but there are often warning signs that precede an episode of psychosis. Knowing what to look for provides the best opportunity for early intervention. Some indications are:

- A worrisome drop in grades or job performance.
- Trouble thinking clearly or concentrating.
- Suspiciousness or uneasiness with others.
- A decline in self-care or personal hygiene.
- Spending much more time alone than usual.
- Strong, inappropriate emotions or having no feelings at all.

Causes

Several factors can contribute to psychosis:

- **Genetics.** While studies are still being conducted to determine the exact genes that cause psychosis, many genes are associated with the development of psychosis. However, just because a person has a gene does not mean that they will experience psychosis.

- **Trauma.** A traumatic event such as a death, war, or sexual assault can trigger a psychotic episode. The type of trauma—as well as a person's age—also affect whether a traumatic event will result in psychosis.
- **Substance use.** The use of marijuana, LSD, amphetamines, and other substances can increase the risk of psychosis in people who are already vulnerable.
- **Physical illness or injury.** Traumatic brain injuries, brain tumors, strokes, HIV, and some brain diseases such as Parkinson's, Alzheimer's, and dementia can sometimes cause psychosis.

Diagnosis

Psychosis is not an illness but a symptom—a component of an illness. Health care providers draw on information from medical and family history along with a physical examination to make a diagnosis. If causes such as a brain tumor, infection, or epilepsy are ruled out, a mental illness might be the cause.

Treating Psychosis

Identifying and treating psychosis as early as possible leads to the best outcomes. With the best chance of preventing illness from progressing, early intervention is always the best approach to treating a mental health condition.

Many specialized centers focus exclusively on psychosis and crisis treatment in youth. In addition to your insurance carrier, primary care doctor, and state or county mental health authorities, you can find help from resources such as the American Psychiatric Association and its state chapters.

Psychotherapy

Therapy is essential to treating psychosis. Some more common therapies include:

- **Cognitive behavioral therapy (CBT)**, which teaches people to observe and then change ineffective patterns of thinking. For psychosis, CBT teaches a patient to critically evaluate their experience to determine whether or not the experience is real.
- **Supportive psychotherapy** teaches patients to cope with the experience of developing and living with psychosis, as therapists attempt to reinforce healthy ways of thinking and reduce internal conflict.
- **Cognitive enhancement therapy (CET)** seeks to build brain capacity through the use of computer exercises and group work. Increasing cognitive functions, such as the ability to organize thoughts, is the ultimate goal.
- **Family psychoeducation and support** helps individuals who are living with psychosis and their families work on bonding, collaborating, problem solving, and learning from each other. For example, NAMI's Family-to-Family program is available across the nation and has been shown to improve family functioning and outcomes in key measures; in this evidence-based practice, positive results were still seen nine months after families took the class.

Medication

Once a diagnosis has been made, a health care provider may work to select a medication that can help to reduce symptoms. Antipsychotics fall into two classes:

- **First generation, or typical, antipsychotics.** First generation antipsychotic medicines work by regulating levels of dopamine in the brain. These medications can cause muscle stiffness and movement problems that can be short (dystonia) or long term (called tardive dyskinesia). Other side effects can also occur.
- **Second generation, or atypical, antipsychotics.** These medications are called atypical because they are less likely to

block dopamine and cause movement disorders. They do, however, increase the risk of weight gain and diabetes. Changes in nutrition and exercise, and possibly medication intervention, can help address these side effects.

The literature on the utility and effectiveness of the use of antipsychotics early in the course of psychosis and emerging schizophrenia is evolving. Check with a doctor to see progress on the research studies in this important area.

Complementary Health Approaches

In one small study, omega-3 fatty acids, commonly found in fish oil, were found to decrease the risk of developing psychosis in young adults and teens who demonstrated early symptoms. Researchers believe that omega-3s may help by replenishing neurons and connections in the brain.

Hospitalization

For acute safety issues, people experiencing psychosis may require sedation in order to be evaluated and some may need to be hospitalized during an episode. Hospital staff will run tests to rule out potential causes for a psychotic episode, such as drugs and alcohol use or another illness. Based on what they find, they will suggest a course of treatment that might include medication, outpatient therapy, or an extended inpatient stay.

Cultural Considerations

People from different cultures have different needs, so working with a professional who is sensitive to cultural interpretations of illness can help improve recovery outcomes. For example, visual or auditory hallucinations with a religious content, such as hearing God's voice, may be viewed as a normal part of religious experience.

SELF-HARM

The urge to self-harm isn't uncommon, especially in adolescents and young adults, though many people keep such habits secret.

With treatment, many people overcome these behaviors. Whether self-harm is a relatively new habit or a longstanding one, patients have the opportunity to improve health and reduce these behaviors. Talking to a doctor or a trusted friend or family member is the first step towards understanding and finding relief from self-harming behaviors.

What is Self-harm?

Any time someone deliberately hurts their own body—inflicting pain on purpose—the activity is classified as self-harm or self-injury. Some people cut their skin with a knife, while others feel an impulse to burn themselves, pull out hair, or pick at wounds to prevent healing. The scars caused by frequent cutting or burning can be permanent, and extreme injuries can even result in broken bones. Those who drink alcohol or do drugs while inflicting self-harm increase the risk of more severe injuries than they intended.

In addition to the physical damage, self-harm causes emotional pain, too. It results in feelings of shame, and takes time and energy away from other valued aspects of life. When students skip classes or young people avoid social situations to prevent people from seeing scars it's a sign that their habit is negatively affecting work and relationships.

Why People Self-harm

When people harm themselves—or think about doing so—it is a sign of emotional distress. If a person continues to use self-harm as a coping mechanism, uncomfortable emotions may grow more intense, so it is important that patients learn other ways to tolerate mental pain and gain strength in the long term.

Self-harm is not a mental illness, but a behavior that indicates a lack of coping skills. Several illnesses are associated with it, including borderline personality disorder, depression, eating disorders, anxiety, and posttraumatic stress disorder. The association with another condition is more likely if additional signs of emotional distress are present. Such signs might include statements of hopelessness or of feeling worthless, poor impulse control, or difficulty getting along with others.

Self-harm occurs most often during the teenage and young adult years, though it can also happen later in life. A person who binge drinks or does drugs is at greater risk of self-injury, because alcohol and drugs lower self-control, and people who have experienced trauma, neglect, or abuse are at the highest risk, such as someone who grew up in an unstable family.

Self-harming urges may start with overwhelming feelings of anger, frustration, or pain. When a person is not sure how to deal with their emotions or learns to hide their emotions as a child, self-harm may feel like a release. Sometimes, self-injury stimulates the body's endorphins or pain-killing hormones, thus raising the mood. Others who don't feel many emotions might cause self-pain in order to replace emotional numbness and feel something "real."

After self-injury, shame and guilt can lead to intense negative feelings, so the person may inflict additional self-harm. Thus, the behavior can become a dangerous cycle and a longtime habit, around which some people even create rituals.

Self-harm is not the same as attempting suicide. However, it is a symptom of emotional pain that should be taken seriously, since a person who is self-harming may be at an increased risk of feeling suicidal. It's important to find treatment for the underlying emotions.

What to Do When Someone Self-harms

If a friend or family member has frequent bruises or bandages—or wears long sleeves and pants even in hot weather—they may be hiding injuries or scars from self-inflicted injuries.

If you're worried that your child might be engaging in self-injury, talk to a medical professional who is familiar with the subject, ideally a psychiatrist. You can also raise the conversation with the child. Ask how life is going. Even if the answer makes you uncomfortable, be prepared to listen. Don't dismiss emotions or try to turn it into a joke. It may be a hard subject for you to understand, so one of the best things you can say is that while you may not fully understand, you'll be there to help.

Tell your child that self-harm isn't uncommon, that doctors and therapists can help, and that you want your child to get treatment, which you will find. Don't try to make the child promise to stop, as it takes more than willpower to quit.

Treatment and Coping

Effective treatments for self-harm can allow a person to feel in control again. Self-harm may feel necessary to manage emotions, so a person will need to learn new coping mechanisms and psychotherapy is important to any treatment plan.

If you take your child to a psychiatrist, the doctor will ask questions about the child's health, life history, and any injurious behaviors in the past and present. This conversation, called a diagnostic interview, may last an hour or more. Doctors can't use blood tests or physical exams to diagnose mental illness, so they rely on detailed information from the child and parents. The more information that the family can provide, the better the treatment plan will be.

Depending on any underlying illness, a doctor may prescribe medication to help with difficult emotions. For someone with depression, for instance, an antidepressant may reduce harmful urges. A doctor will also recommend therapy to help a person learn new behaviors if self-injury has become a habit. Several different kinds of therapy can help, depending on the diagnosis.

- Psychodynamic therapy focuses on exploring past experiences and emotions.
- Cognitive behavioral therapy focuses on recognizing negative thought patterns and increasing coping skills.
- Dialectical behavioral therapy can help a person learn positive coping methods.

If symptoms are overwhelming or severe, a doctor may recommend a short stay in a psychiatric hospital, which provides a safe environment where the patient can focus on treatment.

SLEEP DISORDERS

"Get at least eight hours of sleep per night for optimal health."

Sleep seems like such an easy concept! But in reality, many people experience sleep problems—not getting enough sleep, not feeling rested, and not sleeping well. In healthy people, these issues can lead to difficulty functioning during the daytime and can have unpleasant effects on school, work, and relationships. Many health conditions and mental health conditions can be worsened by sleep-related problems. In fact, in someone who is dealing with mental illness, sleep problems can jeopardize mental health. Sleep is so critical to our well-being, it can make the difference between balanced mental health and full-blown depression or psychotic relapse. Sleep problems can also be secondary to medical illnesses and can indicate an impending condition such as bipolar disorder.

Insomnia

One of the major sleep disorders that people face is insomnia, the inability to get sufficient sleep. More than one-third of Americans report difficulty sleeping, which is characterized by difficulty falling asleep, difficulty staying asleep, or waking up too early in the morning.

Rarely an isolated medical or mental illness, insomnia is more often a symptom of another illness or condition to be investigated in concert with medical doctors. For example, insomnia or other sleep problems can be caused by sleep apnea, a medical condition that affects a person's ability to breathe while sleeping. A doctor or sleep specialist can diagnose sleep apnea and provide treatment to improve sleep.

Insomnia can also be caused by a person's lifestyle or daily schedule. Stress, travel, and other life events can cause short-term insomnia, which is very common. Simple "sleep hygiene" interventions such as exercise, a disciplined sleep/wake schedule, and changing the bedroom environment can generally relieve occasional insomnia. Long-term insomnia lasts for more than three weeks and should be investigated by a physician with a potential referral to a sleep disorder specialist, psychiatrist, neurologist, or pulmonologist who has expertise in sleep disorders.

Cause and Effect

More than half of insomnia cases are related to depression, anxiety, or psychological stress. Often, the qualities of a person's insomnia and their other symptoms can be helpful in determining the role of mental illness in a person's inability to sleep. For example, early morning wakefulness along with low energy, inability to concentrate, sadness, and a change in appetite or weight can signal depression. On the other hand, increased energy accompanied by a sudden dramatic decrease in sleep or a decrease in the need for sleep may indicate mania.

Many anxiety disorders are associated with difficulties sleeping. Obsessive-compulsive disorder (OCD) is frequently associated with poor sleep. Panic attacks during sleep may suggest a panic disorder, and poor sleep resulting from nightmares may be associated with posttraumatic stress disorder (PTSD).

Substance abuse can also cause problems with sleep. While a limited quantity of alcohol is sedating, alcohol intoxication can cause wakefulness and disturb sleep patterns. Hallucinogenic drugs, such as LSD, ecstasy, and Molly, are also associated with sleep disruptions. While some sedative medications may cause sleepiness during intoxication, these same medications can disturb sleep and cause serious sleep problems in people who are addicted to or withdrawing from them.

The treatment of sleep disorders has been studied in relationship to schizophrenia, ADHD, and other mental illnesses. Studies indicate that poor sleep significantly worsen the symptoms of many mental health issues, and severe sleep problems can decrease the effectiveness of certain treatments. All of the scientific data shows this connection between medical and mental illnesses: Good sleep is necessary for recovery—or prevention—in both types of conditions.

Treatment

Good sleeping habits are the first-line treatment for insomnia. Called sleep hygiene, these habits include maintaining a regular sleep schedule, avoiding stimulating activities like exercise before bed, and having a comfortable sleep environment. It's also important to take care of any underlying physical conditions that may be causing sleep problems. When these are not enough, other treatment options can be considered.

- **Relaxation techniques.** Deep breathing, progressive muscle relaxation, and mindfulness can help people become aware of their body and decrease anxiety about going to sleep.
- **Medication.** Many psychiatric drugs are used to promote sleep in people with insomnia. Doctors don't generally recommend staying on medication for more than a few weeks but there are a few medications that have been approved for long term use. With any of these medications, patients should be careful to avoid the risk of over-sedation, which can occur when they take these medications along with other drugs or alcohol.
- **Herbal remedies.** Melatonin and valerian root are two herbal remedies that are available over-the-counter at many pharmacies and other locations. The effectiveness of these treatments has not been proven for most people, and neither treatment has been approved by the FDA.
- **Sleep restriction.** This form of therapy increases "sleep efficiency" by decreasing the amount of time that a person spends in bed awake. This involves very strict rules regarding the amount of time that a person spends lying in bed at night, which gradually increases over time.
- **Cognitive behavioral therapy.** This therapy can help patients control or eliminate negative thoughts and worries that keep them awake.
- **Light therapy.** Also known as phototherapy, this can be specifically helpful in people with a condition called "delayed sleep phase syndrome."
- **Exercise is associated with improved sleep quality.** Talk with your health care provider about the kind of exercise that will work for you. For many people the timing and type of exercise they participate in can improve their sleep habits.

Extensive information is available online from the National Sleep Foundation, but anyone who has a debilitating sleep challenge should consult their health care provider.

Chapter 4—Treatment Options

Treatment options for mental illness include medications, therapy, and experimental treatments as well as outpatient programs, residential treatment, and hospitalization. The biggest challenge, sometimes, is finding the right balance of all these options to best help your child, and your family, to manage their mental illness.

This chapter outlines in more detail what these treatment options include in order for you to have a better understanding of what they entail as you discuss your child's treatment with your health care team.

Medications

Like all medications, there are benefits and side effects to any medication option, and what works for some children will not work for others, particularly when a comorbid condition is present. Medications can be a long-term necessity, or can be a key short-term component that reduces symptoms in order to allow time for other supportive treatment options to be put in place.

Talk with your medical provider any time a medication seems to be less effective or possibly causing new symptoms. Be aware, too, that some medications are more addictive than others or require a controlled withdrawal if being stopped or changed.

- **Anti-Anxiety Medications** – Anti-anxiety medications include several different types of medications used to treat the symptoms of anxiety disorders. Each works in a different part of the brain or nervous system to lessen anxiety. They also each come with their own set of potential side effects that can, ironically, sometimes include anxiety. Medications prescribed as anti-anxiety medications include:
    - Antidepressants – Antidepressants generally work in an inhibitory manner, preventing the brain from reabsorbing the neurotransmitters serotonin or noradrenaline, or brain enzymes like monoamine oxidase. These substances play a role in mood stabilization and the function of these medications is to keep more of these chemicals in circulation within the brain. Side effects can include nausea, anxiety or a possible increase in suicidal thoughts.
    - Antipsychotics – There are two general classes of antipsychotic medications – referred to as "typical" or "atypical" – that work mainly by controlling the effects of dopamine in the brain. They are also commonly prescribed for schizophrenia or bipolar disorder. Side effects can include a range of symptoms from dry mouth to movement disorders (thought to be less likely with atypical antipsychotics).
    - Beta blockers – Beta blockers work in either the heart or blood vessels to block epinephrine (adrenaline). This action lowers blood pressure and causes the heart rate to slow which often has a calming effect.
    - Benzodiazepines and anxiolytics – Commonly known as tranquilizers, these types of medications make the nerves in the brain less sensitive to stimulation by increasing GABA (gamma aminobutyric acid) which suppresses or inhibits the communication of neurotransmitters between the brain cells. They are also common as muscle relaxers.
- **Antidepressants** – Antidepressants prevent the brain from reabsorbing mood-influencing neurotransmitters, like serotonin or noradrenaline, or brain enzymes like monoamine oxidase. The increased presence of these neurotransmitters or enzymes is thought to improve the communication between brain cells and

thus allow the brain to better regulate moods. Their action is often reflected in their name of "reuptake inhibitors."

There are generally five types of antidepressants prescribed, each targeting a specific neurotransmitter or enzyme, or combination:

- Selective Serotonin Reuptake Inhibitors (SSRIs)
- Serotonin and Noradrenaline Reuptake Inhibitors (SNRIs)
- Monoamine Oxidase Inhibitors (MAOIs)
- Noradrenaline and Specific Serotoninergic Antidepressants (NASSAs)
- Tricyclic Antidepressants (TCAs)

- **Antipsychotic Medications** – Most commonly prescribed for schizophrenic disorders or mania (including bipolar disorder), antipsychotic medications work mainly by controlling the effects of dopamine in the brain, and also impact the effects of serotonin, noradrenaline, and acetylcholine within the brain. The two general types of antipsychotic medications – typical and atypical – can have different side effects from dry mouth to weight gain to movement disorders.

- **Mood Stabilizers** – Mood stabilizers are a class of medications used to treat mood disorders that typically have intense or sustained mood shifts, like bipolar disorder, schizoaffective disorder or borderline personality disorder. Many medications referred to as mood stabilizers are also used as anticonvulsants or antipsychotics. Depending on the type of medication, a mood stabilizer medication targets the synapse between neurons, a specific enzyme of the brain, or sodium channels connected to the glutamate system within the brain.

- **Non-stimulants** – The only non-stimulant drug currently approved by the FDA is Atomoxetine, an antidepressant medication in the Selective Norepinephrine Reuptake Inhibitors (SNRIs) class. It is most commonly prescribed to treat ADHD, and is thought to have fewer serious side effects than typical stimulant medications although is also viewed as being less effective than stimulant medications.

- **Stimulants** – "Stimulants", often referred to as "uppers," is an umbrella term used to describe a group of medications that increase the action of the central nervous system and body. Not surprisingly, they include a range of prescription, performance-enhancing, and recreational drugs both legal and illegal. Because of the many medications that are included in this category, it is impossible to pinpoint the exact action of each type of drug (although it's generally thought to increase the release of dopamine) but the effect is typically an elevated mood, increased energy or focus, and an improved sense of well-being. This also makes them very prone to abuse, and the side effects can be mild to dangerous.

Clinical/Hospital Treatments

- **Brain Stimulation Therapies** – Brain stimulation therapies treat mental illness and other disorders like epilepsy by activating (or inhibiting) specific areas of the brain with electricity or with magnetic fields that are either applied externally or via an implant placed in the brain. While some of these therapies are still in experimental stages, others are also showing promise in treating severe mental illnesses. Brain stimulation therapies are generally only considered for mental illnesses that have not shown improvement through other treatment combinations of medication and/or psychotherapy or behavioral therapies.

- **Electroconvulsive Therapy (ECT)** – Electroconvulsive therapy was developed as a treatment for epilepsy but has also been used for treating extreme depression, bipolar disorder or schizophrenia. This is a medical procedure done under anesthetic that uses electrodes to pass a small current through a specific area of the brain, either from both sides (bilaterally) or from one side (unilaterally). ECT is considered to be effective fairly quickly (usually people see improvement in a matter of weeks) and with reduced risk of relapse. Common side effects include headaches, stomach issues or memory loss.

- **Repetitive Transcranial Magnetic Stimulation (rTMS)** - Repetitive transcranial magnetic stimulation uses a magnet to activate certain areas of the brain. Considered more specific in its application, rTMS was approved in 1985 as a treatment for depression, anxiety, psychosis and other mental illnesses. It is a non-invasive procedure that applies a magnet coil to the skull to administer an electromagnetic pulse to the brain, and generally has minor side effects. rTMS is still considered a new treatment therapy with no information available about long-term results or side effects.

- **Vegus Nerve Stimulation (VNS)** – The vegus nerve is a prominent nerve that branches through the body to deliver signals from major organs, like the heart, lungs and intestines, to the areas of the brain that control moods, sleep and other functions. In VNS therapy, a small device is implanted under the skin and programmed to deliver electrical pulses through the left vegus nerve. VNS was originally developed to treat seizures but a co-response was noted in its effect on certain mood disorders as well. It is thought to play a role in treating mental illness by altering the levels of certain neurotransmitters in the brain. Side effects may include breathing problems, neck pain, voice changes or discomfort around the device site.

- **Deep Brain Stimulation (DBS)** – Deep brain stimulation provides continuous electrical stimulation via a pair of electrodes implanted in the brain. Developed as a treatment to control symptoms of Parkinson's Disease, DBS also has shown some help in treating obsessive compulsive disorder or major depression but its use is still considered experimental. Implanting the electrodes requires brain surgery, plus implanting two generator devices in the chest, with all the risks normally associated with these major surgeries, including movement disorders, disorientation, sleep dysfunction, stroke or infection.

Psychological & Behavioral Therapies

- **Applied Behavior Analysis (ABA)** – Behavior analysis examines how learning takes plan, and applied behavior analysis uses these principles to encourage a positive change in behavior. A simple example to understand this therapy model is the idea of positive reinforcement. When a good or desirable behavior is rewarded, it is more likely the child will repeat it. Other practices include modeling or teaching looking, listening or imitating skills. ABA has proven to be an effective set of strategies that can be applied both in a structured setting like a classroom, or a personal or family setting as well.

- **Cognitive Behavioral Therapy (CBT)** – Cognitive behavioral therapy focuses on mood management and impulse control through improving emotional awareness and coping skills. It works to change challenging behavior by teaching the child different strategies for processing their thoughts and emotions and providing them a more stable emotional state to make choices from.

- **Dialectical Behavioral Therapy (DBT)** – Dialectical Behavioral Therapy combines Cognitive Behavioral Therapy with a component of meditation or "mindfulness." DBT focuses on four areas: mindfulness (or self-awareness), interpersonal effectiveness, emotional regulation, and distress tolerance. Combining individual therapy sessions and group skills sessions, DBT focuses on teaching behavioral skills to manage problematic emotional extremes. DBT was developed as a treatment for Bipolar Disorder but has been effective in treating other mood disorders as well.

- **Sensory Integration (SI)/Occupational Therapy** – SI therapy focuses on fine motor skills and sensory interaction to improve/reduce their reactions to problematic sensory stimulation. In effect, the goal is to teach children better awareness and control of their bodies and can reduce clumsiness, hand-eye coordination and anxiety related to sensory overstimulation.

- **Exposure and Response Prevention Therapy (ERP)** - Exposure and response therapy works to gradually reduce fearful or out-of-context reactions to situations or stimuli through controlled exposure to the triggers. It's commonly used for various forms of anxiety or OCD. By consciously engaging in low-key fears and learning not to engage the stimuli (a practice called Ritual Prevention), ERP can be an effective coping strategy to help mitigate problematic symptoms or behaviors.

- **Eye Movement Desensitization and Reprocessing (EMDR)** – EMDR is a nontraditional therapy method for reducing negative feelings associated with a traumatic experience, and is commonly used for treating PTSD or certain anxiety disorders. The treatment combines recalling the painful event while focusing on an eye-movement technique, with the underlying hypothesis being that this dual approach creates emotional distance from the event to let the person fully process and diminish the negative emotions and replace them with more positive ones.

- **Psychodynamic Psychotherapy** – Psychodynamic psychotherapy is a talk therapy technique that does not target a specific behavior or symptom but instead takes a "global" or "depth" approach that focuses on the person's unconscious urges, needs, feelings and desires with the intention of raising self-awareness that would produce a cathartic or natural change in behaviors and thoughts. Sessions are generally very open-ended and patient-guided.

- **Assertive Community Treatment (ACT)** – Assertive community treatment is a highly integrated approach to delivering mental health services through outpatient services that encompass work, physical health, money management, social relationships or independent living for those whose mental illness significantly limits functionality in these areas. Programs can vary widely in different regions but attempt to provide balanced, comprehensive support to the individuals they serve.

- **Family-Focused Therapy** – Family-focused therapy, as the name suggests, works with individual families as a whole to provide support for the emotional and relational challenges of having a family member with a mental illness. Family-focused therapy can help the family members identify personal challenges, set effective coping, disciplinary or communication strategies, and set realistic or progressive expectations for each member of the family.

- **Group and Peer Support** – Peer groups or support groups connect people living with similar conditions and can be beneficial in providing a place to be with others who "get it." Peer groups can be either for an individual chronic health condition like a particular mental illness, or for the caregivers that support them. They can take the form of formal, moderated group meetings, or can be a network that connects through phone messaging, emails, forums, a website or social media. Peer support can be very effective although it's also wise to provide some supervision or accountability for groups your child may connect to that is not moderated.

- **Interpersonal Therapy** – Interpersonal therapy is usually a short-duration talk therapy that focuses on the relationships in a person's family or peer group and how the person sees their role within those relationships and manages problems that may occur in those relationships.

- **Supportive Therapy** – Supportive therapy uses a variety of therapy treatment models to provide their patient with practical and effective strategies to reinforce healthy thought processes and increase the ability to adapt to new emotional or mental realities. A support therapist generally works to build trust and is often more involved on a personal level with the emotional wellbeing of their patient, providing encouragement, information and sympathy along with information and strategic information.

- **Other Therapists and Specialists** – There are a number of therapists that combine the therapy approaches listed above, or offer complimentary or more holistic approaches for specific disorders. As with any therapist or specialist, be sure to provide all information relating to your child's treatment to ensure the most positive outcomes.

Complementary and Alternative Medicine (CAM)

- **Acupuncture** – Acupuncture is based on traditional Chinese medicine and involves the insertion of thin needles into the body. There are different types of acupuncture that include applying heat, pressure or laser light to the needle although none have proven in studies to have significant or consistent results. Most commonly used for pain relief, acupuncture has been used for other ailments as well. Related practices include electroacupuncture, cupping, acupressure or fire needle acupuncture.

- **Exercise** – Exercise is a consistent and sometimes underused method of regulating mood, improving breathing, and combating stress. Physical activity can provide mental as well as physical benefits and should be included in most treatment plans at a level appropriate to the abilities and type best suited to your child. If poor coordination or extreme risk-taking is part of your child's mental illness, talk with a professional to find the best exercise option. As a family, it benefits everyone to take part in some form of exercise.

- **Light Therapy** – Light therapy, or phototherapy, uses a light box to expose a person to full spectrum light that mimics daylight to regulate the hormone melatonin and other neurotransmitters linked to mood and sleep. It is frequently used to treat Seasonal Affective Disorder (SAD) and other depression or sleep disorders.

- **Stress and Relaxation Techniques** including "Self-Soothing" and Mindfulness – Breathing or relaxation techniques can be useful to calm the sympathetic nervous system, release tense muscles, calm heart rate and reoxygenate the body, all of which can reduce anxiety, and provide an immediately available benefit for managing emotions. "Self-soothing" refers to a person's ability to stay calm or regain their composure when emotions are at stressful levels, and methods generally include distraction by focusing on a pleasurable sensory experience like a scent, sound, texture or taste.

- **Meditation, Faith and Prayer** – Similar in effect to many relaxation techniques, meditation or prayer often serve to bring a sense of calm or peace by focusing on a specific theme or thoughts directed to God. A person's faith may provide comfort and community in navigating the experiences of a mental illness, although it may also provide a source of contention or self-doubt. As has been said several times already, your child's mental illness is NOT your fault. Focus on what is helpful, peaceful or relaxing in the moments that you need to find calm.

- **Supplements** – Supplements are any dietary product meant to be support possible shortages in vitamins, minerals or food categories in your child's diet. Results vary widely on the effectiveness of supplements to reduce or improve symptoms in various mental illnesses, and your medical team should always be informed of any supplements being given to your child as some will impact or interact with their prescribed medications.

- **Nutritional Counseling and Changes in Diet** – A healthy diet is the foundation of both physical and mental health but it may also be that your child is sensitive to specific food substances. Common adverse food reactions include gluten, egg, lactose or peanut allergies, along with some preservatives or dyes, and careful observation should be made of any foods that seem to trigger or increase your child's symptoms. Consulting with a nutritional counsellor can be very helpful in identifying possible food culprits, and your medical team should be notified of any extreme changes in diet or eating habits.

Self-management Strategies and Education

- **School Assistance/Advocacy** – Schools are required by federal mandate to provide services to assist all disabled students, and the programs of your school district can be a valuable asset. These should include an Individualized Education Program (IEP) that is updated yearly for your child, along with strategic assistance to help your child manage their class settings and educational goals. Not all school districts do this well, though, and it may be necessary to find, or hire, an advocate to mediate these issues with your child's school.

- **Service Animals** – Many people with mental illness can manage a routine life very well with the assistance of a specially-trained service animal. Usually dogs, these animals can help with household tasks, navigation while walking, seizure warnings, or other safety skills.

- **Specialized Classes and Skills Training** – Knowledge is power, and in many cases a better understanding of a particular mental illness or training in managing its symptoms can be a huge step forward in a successful treatment plan. Training and education are available on a wide variety of mental health topics and can provide key steps in managing your child's illness or your ability to be their best advocate. Contact your local NIMH chapter or visit www.nimh.org to see what classes or training might be available to you or your child.

Inpatient Treatment/Hospitalization

In-patient treatment or hospitalization (see Chapter 6) is usually required for:

- Emergency situations marked by extreme symptoms, or the possibility that the person will harm themselves or others.
- Situations where close supervision is necessary, either to manage medications, to supervise safety, or to monitor withdrawal from substance addiction.

The cost and coverage of different treatments and facilities will vary greatly, and you will have to navigate your insurances process to determine what is covered and what is not.

The next section of this book will dive into some of the practical realities of making that happen.

Part II: Practical Tips

One of the most difficult challenges with many mental illnesses and disorders is that the brain might not recognize dysfunction in itself. The brain might not know that it's not working right, a condition called anosognosia (see Chapter 4 for more information). As a result, patients who are suffering from mental disorders might not agree that mental illness is their problem, and it can be hard to convince them.

Getting someone to accept mental health treatment is less challenging if you are dealing with a mentally ill child because you are in charge; you can take your son or daughter to treatment, make sure they take their medication, or even admit your child for inpatient care. And if your child faces legal problems, those are also not as serious for a juvenile as for an adult.

But this control (almost always) goes away when your mentally ill teenager turns eighteen. Most mentally ill adults have all the rights of any other adults—including privacy—as well as the responsibilities— including legal consequences—unless and until those rights are legally revoked. This makes it imperative that you do all you can to get your struggling and suffering child—especially a teenager— appropriate and effective help as soon as possible.

As the parent of a mentally ill child, you must primarily be the advocate. You will find doctors and other caregivers, coordinate insurance benefits and payments, perhaps, research inpatient institutions. You will collaborate with your child's teacher and principal, and maybe fight with the school district. You will deal with your child's friends and their parents, and you may need to work with police, juvenile hall, and the court system. Through it all, you will also need to take care of yourself, maybe your spouse, and maybe other children, as well. It's a lot to do! You can do it, but you might need some help.

This part of the book will help you get that support, and assist you in navigating through the maze of services, caregivers, advocates, and resources that are available to you so you can find and benefit from all that support.

I know how exhausting it can be to parent and manage your child's mental illness, school issues and insurance denials. If you need help, you might consider hiring a denials management company or attorney who is well-versed in health insurance or education laws specifically for mental health.

The National Alliance on Mental Illness, at www.nami.org, provides many resources for mentally ill patients and family members. With local affiliates across the country, NAMI is making great strides in providing education and support, raising awareness, and advocating for change. Anyone can take classes, participate in support groups, get involved, donate, or share their story. I hope you will visit www.NAMI.org for information.

Our Story Continues…

I was a blithering mess after leaving my 13-year-old daughter at that first treatment center, and was so relieved that my mom had made the trip with me. I don't know if I could have driven myself home.

Over and over, Jeff and I continued to question our decision as even after Chloe was in treatment for a month, we weren't seeing the progress that we expected. We moved her to another facility, closer to home, and within days, Chloe began to thrive and show growth and improvement. Finally, we received a diagnosis of Asperger's Syndrome and it was like a light went off. This knowledge dramatically helped us understand and parent her.

We were encouraged. Through the next six weeks, Chloe learned new skills to cope with her emotions, and she seemed to have a new sense of responsibility and accountability for life and her actions. She was able to have home visits with us on the weekends, adding days as the weeks went by. As the summer wound down, we decided Chloe was ready to come home. She had two weeks of summer break remaining, which she relished before school started up again.

For about a year, Chloe's treatment was very positive and successful. She attended school about 75% of the time, took responsibility for herself, helped with chores, followed our rules, and lived on a reasonable schedule. And she was happy about herself. Even her teachers remarked about the change in Chloe and how she seemed like another person.

Through seventh and eighth grades, Chloe was enrolled in a small charter school that specializes in educating bright yet different youth who have been failed by our traditional public school system. Attending school part time, she learned to manage her anxiety with new skills, which the school fosters and encourages. Her social skills improved tremendously and, as a freshman, she loved school. Embracing a full-time schedule, she was determined to keep on track in order to graduate in four years.

But just like life, mental illness is often messy. Chloe finished her freshman fall and winter terms with good grades. But her confidence quickly fell by the wayside as she got deeper and deeper in with the wrong crowd.

She was doing so well. She was on track with school, focused and getting good grades, and there was finally hope that she would graduate high school.

Then winter break hit and too much idle time spelled trouble for Chloe, whose brain lacks executive functioning, good judgment and impulse control. Poor decisions lead to more poor decisions and the reality for many of the "friends" she hung out with is that there was little structure and no expectation for them to attend school, work or plan for a future.

One night, towards the end of winter break, Chloe set up for a fight with a girl that was supposed to be her "friend," most likely because of a comment she unknowingly and flippantly made. The video of the fight went viral. Between the betrayal of her friends and the social media frenzy, it was enough to set Chloe back a few years. She fell into a deep depression and funk. Her behaviors were reminiscent of when she was 10. She couldn't focus at school and eventually dropped out in late January for the remainder of the year.

Though initially in denial, we had known since the end of that second term that the time would come when we'd have to send her to treatment, again, and her 15th birthday in May was our next sign that she needed help. Another set of friends. This time, one had a bad home life and stayed at our house for refuge. She also used drugs (not *in our house, I'd tell myself) to escape her horrible home reality. Chloe felt bad for her friend and wanted to help her, but was unable to see that the friend only used her for money and to steal from our family to exchange for drugs. It took Chloe about a month for her to realize that her "friend" would choose drugs over her every time.*

The third and final indicator occurred in July. Again, new friends; every time one relationship would go wrong, Chloe would desperately seek new ones, hoping to find people she could trust, who were loyal and accepted her for who she was. Unfortunately, the outcome was always similar. This time, she had unknowingly invited a dealer into our home. My younger daughter witnessed through an outside window suspicious activity among a few of the boys and when I arrived home frantically told me what she'd seen. I raced into the house and into Chloe's room and immediately found the evidence I needed to kick those kids out of our house.

Feeling defeated and hopeless, Chloe wrote in a post, "...I'm always put down and I am never ever happy with myself. I always find a way to F@#% something important up and I don't know how to stop it. I just wanna have a nice life but I can't because I'm a mentally-challenged person. I didn't even ask to be mentally-challenged, I was born with it...I'm literally so close to ending my life, you don't understand. Yeah, I look happy on the outside but on the inside I'm just a disaster and disappointment."

The next morning, Jeff and I had a session with our therapist and for the third time, she told us Chloe needed intervention. The option was a future of probable drug addiction, legal problems, or worse, suicide or death.

We knew this round of treatment had to be different than last time. One that was specialized, focused on Chloe's Asperger's traits, bipolar diagnosis and all the other comorbid diagnoses that came with it. We also knew an equine component would be critical for her healing and learning, and that our family's therapy and education would also be instrumental to her success. Though the $11,000 monthly tuition was daunting and almost cost-prohibitive, we decided it was the step we had to take and were more than willing to sacrifice our retirement savings to make it happen.

Chloe was, and is, absolutely worth it.

Chapter 5—Finding Help...and Paying for It

GETTING REAL: REBECCA

Diane hoped to adopt a child and was excited when a friend told her about a pregnant 15-year-old she knew. The girl sounded great. She didn't do drugs or drink and she had taken good care of herself in pregnancy despite her young age, the friend said. When the baby arrived, Diane named her Rebecca as she settled into a role she'd only imagined: Mom. She thought it was going well.

But at Rebecca's three-month checkup, the pediatrician asked about the infant's development, and then he paused. This child, he told her, has major issues. Diane was shocked, then heartbroken, as the doctor delivered his diagnosis: The infant suffered from learning disabilities caused by fetal drug and alcohol syndrome.

At that moment, Diane had no idea how completely Rebecca's issues would dominate the next two decades of her life. Fetal alcohol syndrome was only the first of the labels Rebecca would collect. As she grew, several others were to follow: Asperger's syndrome. Autism. And, when the girl was 12, bipolar disorder.

Taking Your Child to the Pediatrician

In medicine, with any disease or disorder, an effective treatment plan must begin with an accurate diagnosis. So when you are starting out, your goal is to get the most correct diagnosis possible. It may take time and the input of several medical professionals to arrive at the correct diagnosis, especially if several issues are involved. It also means you need to keep an open mind about what's wrong without having an agenda or investing yourself (or anyone else) in this particular diagnosis or that one.

Remember, you're not a doctor and the internet isn't, either. As much as possible, the information you provide to your child's doctor must be based on reality, on what your child feels, on what you've seen and heard, and on what teachers and friends have seen and heard. To that end, the most helpful thing you can do is to keep notes with dates of any incidents that sent up red flags.

When you are ready to take your concerns to a doctor, you can start by making an appointment with your child's pediatrician or your family doctor, but you're still going to need to navigate the healthcare maze. I recommend that you do that by first navigating your insurer's maze. Start with your policy or a summary of benefits provided by your insurance company. You will also need a decent understanding of any copays, deductibles, and coinsurance your insurance company will require. If you can't find this information, you can call the provider or your human resources department and ask them to send you a copy of your complete policy (typically 80+ pages, which is more comprehensive and useful than a summary of benefits and coverage). If you read the section on mental health care, you'll know what your insurer is obligated to provide.

It's also very helpful if you visit your insurance company's website and search for network psychiatrists near your home. Print out your list, and put together some notes about each doctor. If you know anyone whose child has seen a psychiatrist, ask them if they know anyone on your list or recommend a particular doctor that might be in your insurer's network. You can also read online reviews; take them with a grain of salt but note any consistent comments and areas of specialization.

When you go to the appointment with your child's pediatrician or family doctor, it's helpful to bring:

- Your notes about your child's signs of mental illness;
- Your list of providers covered by your insurance.

The pediatrician should do an initial assessment and might have you complete some forms about symptoms. The doctor might also order screening tests to rule out other medical problems. If your child's doctor decides that everything is normal or that the problem is more a matter of parenting, behavior, or emotional issues, listen to your gut. If you want further evaluation, ask for a referral to a psychiatrist. Keep in mind that a psychiatrist's training is specifically on the health and disease of the brain. A pediatrician or general practitioner may miss symptoms or may not have the knowledge to recognize signs of mental illness. Too often, misbehavior is dismissed by the child's stage in life or poor parenting. Remember, if your kid is miserable and so is everyone else in the home, chances are it could be due to an underlying illness. Show the doctor your list of psychiatrists who are in your insurance network and ask if the doctor has any experience or information about any of them.

Seeing a Psychiatrist

As soon as you think you want your child to see a psychiatrist, try to get an appointment on the books. This can be a serious challenge as there are far fewer psychiatrists than the current demand.

If you are having problems getting an appointment with anyone, local offices of the National Alliance on Mental Illness (NAMI) or the Mental Health Association (MHA) may be able to help, and your insurance provider might help you secure an appointment with a network doctor who has appointments available.

Often these insurance issues make the choice of provider for you. If they don't, here are some questions to ask before you choose a doctor:

- Is the doctor board-certified in psychiatry? Child psychiatry?

- Does the doctor specialize in concurrent disorders that my child may be dealing with (such as substance abuse, eating disorders, or learning disabilities)?
- Does the doctor work with a team to provide psychological support, therapy, and/or other treatment services?
- Does the doctor have admitting privileges at a specific hospital?

A High Demand for Psychiatrists

According to a 2015 article by the Huffington Post, fewer than 50,000 psychiatrists were practicing in the United States, and nearly 60% of them were 55 or older.[1] According to the article, "Federal health authorities have designated about 4,000 areas in the U.S. as having a shortage of mental health professionals—areas with more than 30,000 people per psychiatrist." That's a lot of patients going without the care they require. According to the American Academy of Child and Adolescent Psychiatry (AACAP), there is a "workforce crisis" in pediatric psychiatrics.[2] In a 2013 study, the organization found that there are too few child and adolescent psychiatrists to treat the number of children in the United States. This can be attributed to the fact that the specialty is typically underfunded—so doctors won't make as much income—and yet they have to invest extra years of expensive medical training that leads to additional student debt. The result is no surprise: Many psychiatrists are booked for months. Also, some doctors limit the numbers of patients they accept from a given insurance company if the insurer reimburses at a low rate or requires excessive red tape, so more than a few doctors' offices will tell you that the doctor is not accepting new patients—right after you tell them what your insurance is. If you can self-pay, you might find it easier to find a doctor. Also, if you find a highly recommended psychiatrist who is out of network, check with your health insurance regarding coverage. Often, you can opt to pay coinsurance which is more than a co-pay but may be well worth it for a good doctor.

Psychiatry is a science but it looks a lot like art. Generally, psychiatrists can't use physical examinations and lab tests to make diagnoses, but rely on years of medical training as they listen to patients (and their parents) as they discuss what they feel. For the most part, psychiatrists do not do "talk therapy," like psychologists, but spend their time asking questions about symptoms and behaviors, listening to answers, and managing medication, when necessary.

When you take your child to the first appointment with a psychiatrist, you should feel free to ask questions, too. Here are some questions you might ask:

- What is the doctor's treatment philosophy?
- What is the doctor's view on psychotherapy, supplements, alternative medicine (or any other treatments)?
- How long are appointments and how often does the doctor see a patient?
- How far out is the doctor booked for returning patients?
- What do I do if we have an emergency outside office hours?

At this appointment, it is also helpful if you mention any financial issues. If you tell your psychiatrist (and other providers) what insurance you have and what it covers, most of them will try to treat your child within those parameters, as much as possible. Beyond insurance benefits, if your financial resources are very limited, make sure that your doctors also know this, so they can prescribe the most cost-effective solutions and avoid brand name medications, expensive treatments, and unproven alternative therapies.

During this first meeting, if you have any communication problems with the doctor, try to mention the disconnect and see if it improves. If you or your child find it hard to communicate, it might not be a good fit. As you leave your first appointment, you should feel heard and confident that the doctor "gets it." You should also have the sense that both you and the psychiatrist understand the issues, the goals, and the plan for your child. If those things don't feel right, you might see if you can get an appointment with someone else. It may take some time so it's important to continue care with your existing psychiatrist if persistent and serious problems are present or the current treatment is having positive or negative effects.

Insurance Companies: Legal Requirements

In 2008, the Mental Health Parity and Addiction Equity Act set "parity" requirements for mental health services.

Years ago, insurance plans typically covered mental health care at far lower levels than physical illness. In 2008, Congress passed the Paul Wellstone and Pete Domenici Mental Health Parity and Addiction Equity Act (MHPAEA) to ensure equal coverage of treatment for mental illness and addiction. In November 2013, the federal government released rules to implement the law and the Affordable Care Act further impacted the implementation.

Generally, the MHPAEA requires that insurers cannot restrict coverage for mental health and substance abuse services more than coverage for other medical and surgical services. Rather, insurance plans must generally give equal treatment to mental health and substance abuse disorders as to physical disorders and diseases. So, if an insurance plan allows unlimited doctor visits for a physical illness—such as diabetes—it must offer unlimited visits for a mental health disorder, too.

When parity applies, treatment limits and payment amounts must be equal. This applies to in-network and out-of-network care in an inpatient or outpatient setting, intensive outpatient services, partial hospitalization, residential treatment, emergency care, and prescription medications, as well as co-pays, deductibles, maximum out-of-pocket limits, geographic location, facility type, provider reimbursement rates, and the clinical criteria used to approve or deny care.

But, according to the National Alliance for Mental Illness (NAMI), parity is a guarantee of equal coverage, not necessarily good coverage. If your health insurance plan is very limited—meeting the minimum requirements under the Affordable Care Act—then your mental health coverage will be similarly limited, even in a state with a strong parity law or in a plan that is subject to federal parity.[3]

Parity does not apply to every health insurance plan. According to NAMI, the health plans that must follow federal parity include:

- Group health plans for employers with 51 or more employees.
- Most group health plans for employers with 50 or fewer employees (unless they have been "grandfathered"—created before the federal parity laws went into effect).

- The Federal Employees Health Benefits Program.
- Medicaid Managed Care Plans (MCOs).
- State Children's Health Insurance Programs (S-CHIP).
- Some state and local government health plans.
- Plans purchased through the Health Insurance Marketplaces.
- Most individual and group health plans purchased outside the Health Insurance Marketplaces unless "grandfathered."
- Some plans that received an exemption based on cost increases related to parity.

According to NAMI, state parity laws further complicate the issue. Some states have stronger parity laws, which insurance plans have to follow if they do business in those states. But if state laws undermine federal parity, the federal rules prevail.

To find out what kind of plan you have, you can ask your insurance carrier or agent, your plan administrator, or your human resources department.

Is It Covered?

Thanks to parity laws, coverage for mental health diagnosis and treatment must be equal to your coverage for any physical disorder or disease. So, generally, your insurance should cover outpatient care and prescription medications as well as emergency services. They should also cover clinical treatments, psychological and behavioral therapies, and necessary hospitalization or residential treatment—but insurance policies vary and, besides, it can be challenging to prove the necessity of some of these expensive options.

To find out whether prescriptions, treatments, and hospitalizations are covered by your plan, check the information provided by your insurer. Review your policy, summary of benefits and coverage, other materials that your plan sent to you, or your insurer's website to study lists of covered medications and treatments. If you cannot find this information, you can call your insurer directly. The phone number and your membership identification number should be available on your insurance card.

Outpatient Care

Clearly, insurance plans must cover appointments with psychiatrists just as they cover appointments with primary care physicians or other medical specialists. They should also cover appointments with other practitioners, such as psychologists, advanced practice nurses, and therapists, social workers, or counselors. The best treatment plan includes a team approach.

Prescription Medications

Typically, insurance plans do cover mental health prescription medications such as anti-anxiety medications, antidepressants, selective serotonin reuptake inhibitors (SSRIs), antipsychotic medications, mood stabilizers, stimulants, and nonstimulants. Many plans charge a lower co-pay for generic medications and, generally, will make "formulary" medications less expensive for patients. Insurance plans generally do not cover over-the-counter medications, and supplements are generally not covered as they are considered alternative medicine.

Clinical Treatments and Therapies

In addition to all the changes in the health insurance industry, treatment modalities are evolving rapidly and, often, good mental health care also includes other treatments and services from specialists. While a doctor might believe strongly in a given treatment or therapy technique, an insurance company might be skeptical of the benefits. Across the marketplace, insurance policies are inconsistent in what they cover and what you have to contribute in copays, deductibles, and coinsurance.

Again, you need to understand your coverage and know the costs you will incur. It is a good idea to review your plan benefits and conditions before booking appointments for such therapies and, if they are covered, search your insurer's website to find in-network providers, if possible. If you have questions about policy details, visit the insurer's website or call their member services department. Often times, customer service will be the first person you talk to and may not be well-versed on the intricacies of your policy. If you don't feel your questions are being answered or you don't understand, ask for clarification or a supervisor.

If a doctor recommends a particular treatment modality or procedure, it's also a good idea to ask the doctor if most insurance companies consider it effective and—and if they cover it. If your insurer doesn't cover a recommended treatment, talk to the doctor to determine whether the treatment approach is worth your self-payment or if the doctor can suggest a covered alternative.

Since your doctor may want you to consider these treatment modalities for your child, you might want to find out if your insurance provider covers these treatments (each of these is explained in more detail in Chapter 4):

- Brain Stimulation Therapies.
- Cognitive Behavioral Therapy (CBT), which is often covered.
- Electroconvulsive Therapy (ECT).
- Repetitive Transcranial Magnetic Stimulation (RTMS).
- Applied Behavior Analysis (ABA).
- Dialectical Behavioral Therapy (DBT).
- Exposure and Response Therapy (ERT).
- Exposure Response Prevention Therapy (ERP).
- Eye Movement Desensitization and Reprocessing (EMDR).
- Psychodynamic Psychotherapy.
- Assertive Community Treatment.
- Family-Focused Therapy.
- Group and Peer Support.
- Interpersonal Therapy.
- Supportive Therapy.
- Other Therapists and Specialists.

Since the following treatments are considered Complementary and Alternative Medicine (CAM) in mental health care, they are generally not covered:

- Acupuncture.
- Light Therapy.

- Relaxation Techniques.

Inpatient Treatment and Hospitalization

As your child's advocate, you may need to fight for the benefits to which you are entitled.

During our daughter Chloe's first stint in residential treatment, it had been only two weeks when we were informed that our insurer would only cover a few more days, despite the fact that the doctor recommended months of inpatient care.

Although we had paid thousands of dollars in premiums and maximum out-of-pocket costs so that we'd have insurance protection from such expenses, the insurer began denying our claims a week later. Doing the math, I realized that our insurance company's "out-of-pocket" cost was less than ours!

We eventually found a solution that involved switching her insurance and the guidance of the facility we worked with but it was a steep learning curve in navigating the insurance system.

Currently, Chloe is now in her second residential treatment program, we've met our maximum out-of-network, out-of-pocket costs and we have yet to receive a reimbursement from our insurance carrier. It's a private facility and we're required to pay for each month in advance so we have to carry the balance until our insurer pays out.

According to Chloe's treatment facility, our experience with private insurers is very common, and odds are you'll have to dispute your insurer's coverage at some point.

Dealing with Insurance Disputes

If you think your plan is not providing benefits that are included in your policy—or not providing mental health benefits in parity with medical and surgical benefits—you can do something about it!

Federal parity protections mean that if your insurance carrier covers mental health and substance abuse disorders, the benefits have to be the same as "regular" medical benefits.

The federal parity law also applies to the clinical criteria that health insurers use to approve or deny treatment. In deciding whether to pay for a treatment or deny payment for it, insurers determine the medical necessity—whether the treatment is reasonable, necessary, and/or appropriate. These standards must be defined and any current or potential health plan member can request and obtain this information from the insurer. Also, if coverage is denied, you have the right to request and obtain information about the reason for such denial.

The National Alliance on Mental Illness has good information about the parity law, including these signs that an insurer may be violating parity requirements:

- They assess higher costs or allow fewer visits for mental health services than for other kinds of health care.
- They require you to get pre-approval for mental health care but not for other care.
- They deny mental health services, claiming that the services are not considered "medically necessary," but they do not answer a request for their medical necessity criteria.
- You cannot find any in-network mental health providers who are taking new patients, but can find providers for other health care.
- The plan will not cover residential mental health or substance use treatment or intensive outpatient care, but they cover such treatment for other health conditions.[4]

If you suspect that your plan violates parity requirements, review your coverage for all benefits, including mental health care and medical-surgical care. If the mental health care coverage is less (or costs are more) than those for physical health care, your plan might not be in compliance with parity laws. They might be exempt, or they might be in violation. If you think your insurance company is not following parity laws, you can take action:

- File a complaint with your state's Department of Insurance.

- If states do not enforce the law, the Federal Center for Medicaid and Medicare Services can. You can contact them on their help line at 1-877-267-2323, extension 6-1565.
- If your employer provides a "self-insured" plan, the U.S. Department of Labor (DOL) has authority to enforce parity. To find out more, call their toll free number at 1-866-444-3272 or visit the Department of Labor's website at www.dol.gov/ebsa/contactEBSA/consumerassistance.html.

Parity aside, insurance companies still deny claims, but you do not have to accept their denials. According to NAMI, some kinds of mental health services are more often denied than other medical claims. These include residential treatment for mental illness, intensive outpatient treatment, psychological rehabilitation, partial hospitalization and assertive community treatment (ACT), services like psychotherapy, and diagnostic and treatment interventions such as diagnostic assessments and standardized tests.[5] If your insurer denies these sorts of supports and services and you think you are entitled to them, you can file an appeal. NAMI provides solid information about how to do this, and their website includes templates and forms that can help a great deal.

If you decide to appeal the insurance company's denial, be prepared for a hassle, if not a fight.

Enlist Help

Tell your doctor or other mental health professional or provider about the problem. They've been through this before so they may be able to advise you.

If you have the bandwidth, you can go prepare your appeal on your own but, otherwise, medical billing advocates can help you. These professionals help consumers get the care and coverage they are entitled to by navigating all of the paperwork, deadlines and phone calls for you.[6]

Request an Expedited Appeal if it is an Emergency

If your child's condition is urgent because of the denied claim, you can expedite the appeals process. According to the Affordable Care Act, you can only do this if the standard appeal process will "seriously jeopardize" your child's life or ability to "regain maximum function." Obviously, if your child is in a life-threatening situation, this would qualify for the expedited process.

Get Organized

Gather your plan's enrollment materials (the complete policy—usually 80+ pages), statement of benefits and coverage, and any other information that the plan has provided to you). Health insurers are required to provide you with this information so, if you cannot find it in your paperwork or on their website, you can call them and request it.

Find out why the insurance company denied coverage. You have the right to know why they denied coverage and the insurer is required to provide you with this information. Often, they will automatically send an explanation of benefits (EOB) stating why the claim was denied, often in the form of codes indicating their justification for the denial. If you don't receive the EOB, they are required to send it upon request. You can get NAMI's fax template on their website or call or write to the insurer with your request for the reason for the denial. They should respond within thirty days.

Talk to Your Insurance Company

Sometimes, you can solve a lot with a phone call.

If you receive the EOB and still do not understand the reason for the denial, you can call the insurer to get more information about your policy and the insurer's justification. You can also find out whether your services will be covered during the appeal process. Also, importantly, claims are sometimes denied because of clerical errors, so it's a good idea to check for typos in names and policy numbers and ask your insurer about any minor discrepancies you might find.

It's always a good idea to keep notes of the date, time, name of the person you talked to, and the essence of the conversation whenever you contact the insurance company. And, for efficiency, it's also an excellent practice to ask the agent for their name and a call reference number.

Prepare Your Written Appeal

Just like everything else, the appeals process is different with each insurance company, but you have the right to appeal regardless of who provides your health insurance. The EOB should explain your insurer's appeal process or you can find it on the company's website. If anything is unclear, you can call the company and ask them to clarify.

Usually, an appeal has to be submitted within a prescribed period of time. Make sure that you and your provider meet all deadlines in the review or appeals process.

You'll need to submit your appeal in writing, either with a letter or a standard form. Also, NAMI makes template letters available on the association's website. Be sure to include your policy and claim numbers on the appeal letter and any other communications with the insurer. Your appeal letter is your chance to make your case, so it should be as strong as possible. Consider including:

- Your argument for why the coverage should be provided, whether parity laws are being violated and how.
- Supporting evidence such as doctor's recommendations and statements from your insurance policy.
- Any other pertinent information from your child's medical record.
- Letters from any treatment providers who believe the care is necessary.
- *Anything* that supports your position.

Go to the Next Level

If the insurance company denies your appeal, you can initiate an external appeal to have a third party review your claim. Procedures vary by state, though some states have adopted new Affordable Care Act guidelines to help consumers.

If an expedited process is justified, you can initiate the external appeal simultaneously with the first appeal to the insurance company. In this case, a final decision on your claim must come within four days of your request or as quickly as your child's medical condition requires.

If you are not satisfied, you can contact your state's insurance division or consumer services offices for help. NAMI's website[7] includes a directory with names, addresses, and telephone numbers for each state's insurance division. Also, many offer consumer assistance programs to help consumers with health insurance problems. The Centers for Medicare & Medicaid Services at CMS.gov includes a directory of these offices.[8] And the federal Department of Health and Human Services provides further information at MentalHealth.gov.[9]

County, State and Federal Benefits

Since the implementation of the Affordable Care Act, many people who do not have employer-provided health care—and who cannot afford to purchase private insurance—are able to go on government-provided health care plans. States meet these obligations to these consumers in different ways, generally through Medicaid. Medicaid is a joint federal and state program that helps with medical costs for some people with limited income and resources. Each state has different rules about eligibility and applying for Medicaid, and you apply through your state Medicaid program.

The Children's Health Insurance Program (CHIP) is another program offered by each state. CHIP works closely with the state Medicaid program to provide low-cost health coverage to children in families that earn too much money to qualify for Medicaid.

According to the federal Department of Health and Human Services, all state Medicaid programs provide some mental health services and some offer substance use disorder services to beneficiaries. These services often include counseling, therapy, medication management, social work services, peer support, and substance use disorder treatments. While states determine which of these services to cover for adults, Medicaid and CHIP require that children enrolled in Medicaid receive a wide range of medically necessary services, including mental health services. You can find more information on Medicaid, CHIP, and mental health and substance use disorder services at www.medicaid.gov/Medicaid-CHIP-Program-Information/By-Topics/Benefits/Mental-Health-Services.html.[10]

You can also find basic information, including state contact information, to get started at any of these sites:

- Your state's Department of Healthcare services.
- The federal Affordable Care Act website, www.HealthCare.gov.
- The federal Medicare website at www.medicare.gov/your-medicare-costs/help-paying-costs/medicaid/medicaid.html.
- The website of the National Association of Medicaid Directors, which includes a directory of Medicaid directors across the country at www.medicaiddirectors.org/about/medicaid-directors/.

Chapter 6—Hospitalization

GETTING REAL: TREVOR

A pediatric occupational therapist who works with kids with disabilities, Carol knew early on that her son was different.

Trevor was a difficult infant. At his two-month, well-baby checkup his pediatrician noted he exhibited a strong fear of strangers, months earlier than most children begin to show stranger anxiety. That was the first time Carol suspected Trevor wasn't neurotypical.

He was also a sickly child, coming down with the worst case of every childhood illness that was going around. He was diagnosed with benign congenital hypotonia, low muscle tone for no apparent reason.

When he was 2, his daycare provider noted that he was different from the other children in her care and didn't or couldn't interact with them, preferring to do his own thing. That pattern persisted into preschool.

Trevor didn't interact with other kids and Carol didn't know how to help. It was frustrating for them both. Carol, who has been treated for anxiety and depression, as well as anorexia in college, blamed herself for her child's difficulties, thinking that he had social problems because she was a bad parent. She also worried about a genetic component, as her father dealt with anxiety and depression through his life.

Carol and her husband Paul wanted another child, but worried that a baby would face the same struggles as Trevor. When he was 4, they adopted a baby girl, Katie.

In kindergarten, Trevor continued to struggle. Carol didn't know if his social problems were overwhelming him or if something else was interfering with his learning, so she had him tested. The tests showed that he was making academic progress, but she held him back a year, hoping that he might catch up socially.

His social anxiety limited his activity, but he learned to hide the problem. When Carol would give her kids money to go buy soda from a park concession stand, Katie would bound off to make the purchase with Trevor following. When his little sister returned with a drink, Trevor, unable to manage the transaction, would come back money still in hand, saying he wasn't thirsty.

He managed to drift through grade school without major problems. Carol remembers going to parent-teacher conferences where teachers didn't even seem to know who he was in class.

Spelling was particularly difficult for Trevor, and Carol suspected he might have a learning disability. She repeatedly demanded testing, but his school refused. Despite practicing spelling words every night at home with his parents, he would fail tests and be kept inside at recess as punishment. When he was around 11 Carol and Paul again turned to private testing, which confirmed Trevor had a learning disability.

Trevor's problems in school ramped up in middle school, and his pediatrician diagnosed him with social anxiety disorder.

He met with a counselor, but couldn't handle high school. He skipped class, preferring to spend the day walking around alone instead of facing the crowded hallways and classrooms. He was sometimes suicidal. Carol recalls finding a noose hanging in the garage one day.

Around age 14, Trevor overdosed on drugs, emptying the family's medicine cabinets and swallowing everything he could find — aspirin, his mother's hormone replacement therapy, pain pills left from past medical procedures. His parents rushed him to the emergency room where doctors could treat the overdose, but told Carol and Paul that *no mental health services were available locally for teens. A psychiatric hospital in a large city across the state could take him for inpatient treatment.*

Isolated in the waiting room, Carol and her husband struggled to figure out what was best for their son. Carol recalls her husband, who never cries, sobbing over the difficult decisions. They decided to send Trevor and hired a secure transport service to take him there from the local hospital. He left, screaming, in the middle of the night.

Hospitalization didn't work for Trevor. He was often in isolation and at other times lodged with adults. Rather than help, the experience caused post-traumatic stress disorder.

For Carol, Trevor's teen years were hell and she knows the turmoil in his brain must have been even worse for him. He saw string of counselors, but sometimes when Carol drove him to appointments, he would refuse to get out of the car. She would tell him that she wouldn't drive him home until he went inside, so he would walk home rather than attend counseling.

During her son's struggles with mental illness, Carol also floundered without support, pulling away from friends and family she didn't think could handle the challenges she was dealing with. She felt alone, missing the network that she saw for parents of kids with other developmental disabilities. She was plagued with guilt, sure she had failed her son, but still working hard to raise her daughter normally. The stress of work, parenting and maintaining her marriage drove her to exhaustion, causing her to collapse at work shortly before Trevor's overdose landed him in the hospital. She was hospitalized for three days, but tests found no physical cause.

Carol acknowledges that she and Paul struggled to support one another. At one point he developed a close friendship with another woman, whose husband was gripped with mental illness. The relationship left Carol feeling like she didn't have enough to offer her husband. They went through lots of counseling and grew closer in their united efforts to help Trevor. Often though, they didn't know how to help him.

One evening shortly after Trevor turned 18, a confrontation erupted and he grabbed a kitchen knife, threatening to kill his family and himself. Carol called 911 as she and her daughter fled the house. Carol said a counselor had previously told the family that it might take involvement with the criminal justice system for Trevor to get the mental health help he needed. However, he got no mental health resources when he was arrested. When police arrived, Carol asked them to take Trevor to the hospital, but they took him to jail on a menacing charge. He was convicted and left with a criminal record.

As I've said, our systems and resources to support the mentally ill are severely lacking. Nowhere is this more true than in inpatient treatment services.

A detective friend recently told me that our local police department, which serves roughly 70,000 residents, takes ten to fifteen people to the hospital each day due to some sort of mental disturbance. What happens from there, he said, is another story. If there's room, the hospitals admit them to the psychiatric unit but, more often than not, they "treat" them and send them home.

Unfortunately for youth, intensive treatment for mental illness can be just as difficult to obtain unless you're on state assistance or the youth is violent or a danger to self or others. Patients who have private insurance often find that their insurers are reluctant and unwilling to pay for long-term treatment. After all, it can be very expensive.

During one of our daughter's stays in residential treatment, our insurance company began denying coverage for Chloe's care after two weeks—and we learned that this was typical in the industry. When we moved Chloe to another facility, the administration was able to prove a certificate of need for her, so that the state covered the remainder of her treatment. Otherwise, our daughter's daily fee would have been $450. How many families can afford more than $13,000 per month? For most of us, this would be a major hardship, if not out of the question. Our daughter—indeed, our whole family—would have suffered a great deal.

132

For Chloe, residential treatment has been very effective, a game-changer. Early intervention and intensive treatment have been critical, and I know it could be with other families too. I wish our system could do the same for other youth and families who would benefit from these services.

When is Hospitalization Necessary?

Most people who deal with mental health conditions do not ever need to be hospitalized or receive inpatient treatment at a residential facility. But an individual may need to be hospitalized when:

- They need to be closely monitored in order to be accurately diagnosed and/or to have medications adjusted or stabilized.
- They are experiencing an acute crisis episode.
- They have had an encounter with a first responder such as the police or a paramedic.

Hospitalization can be voluntary or not. A voluntary hospitalization is when the person decides it is the best strategy, or when they agree to go at the insistence of a parent or professional. Patients can see such hospitalizations as opportunities to recover from a mental health crisis with consistent medical attention and without daily stressors, such as school responsibilities and family interactions. In a perfect world, our mentally ill loved ones would agree to appropriate help when they need it. Unfortunately, this isn't how it usually works.

Parents, working in concert with their child's doctor, may have to make the decision to hospitalize a child who does not want to go. Depending on circumstances, this can be extremely difficult. Such a choice is clear when children are so ill that they are at risk of hurting someone else, hurting themselves, or if there is a risk of suicide. But lots of times, the circumstances are not that clear, and parents agonize over these decisions, wracked with guilt and shame, fear and dread, indecision and resolve. Making all that emotion worse, families often have to wait weeks or even months for a bed to become available and, when it does, it may be hours away from home.

Just because a doctor prescribes inpatient care, your insurer might not agree to pay for it. An emergency room doctor once told me that insurance companies almost never cover *voluntary* hospitalizations, so it seems families will struggle either way. See the previous chapter for help in dealing with insurance coverage for inpatient care.

In prescribing inpatient treatment, your child's doctor should guide you in the process of finding and choosing a facility. Facilities vary, depending on the level of care your child needs. Generally, the types of 24-hour inpatient facilities include:

- Psychiatric hospitals or psychiatric units in general hospitals.
- Residential care in a residential setting.
- State psychiatric hospitals for patients on state benefit plans.

Facilities generally provide intensive settings and crisis stabilization with close supervision, observation, assessment, and intervention, as well as therapeutic activities and treatment options. In addition to medications, individualized treatment might include psychotherapy, behavior management, and family counseling. School may or may not be provided. Here are some questions you might ask before choosing a facility for your child:

- Can family members visit? When and for how long?
- Will my child be allowed to make and receive phone calls?
- What should we pack?
- Will my child share a room with someone else? What if there are problems?
- Can my child walk around the facility? Are there restrictions on where patients can and cannot go?
- How long will my child be at the facility? Who makes this decision?
- Is therapy in a group setting or one-on-one? Is it part of my child's treatment plan?
- Can parents discuss treatment with the doctor or therapist? When? How often? Will we be advised of changes in treatment?
- What are the goals of this treatment?
- Will my child undergo tests during treatment? Can we refuse these tests?
- Do you have daily schedules with set times for activities, treatments, medications, curfew, and bedtime?
- What types of activities will my child participate in?

- Will my child continue schoolwork during inpatient care? If classes are offered, what are they and who teaches them?

Involuntary Psychiatric Hold

Called different things in different jurisdictions, a psychiatric hold authorizes police officers or medical professionals to involuntarily confine a person who seems to be gravely disabled or a danger to self or others due to a mental disorder. The requirement of "grave disability" or "danger to self or others" is intended to prevent people from being institutionalized against their will, but to help those who are incapable of making their own medical treatment decisions.

Unfortunately, in practice, someone is not usually considered a "danger to self or others" if they are being disruptive or erratic, threatening, throwing things, or even—sometimes—hurting themselves or someone else. Often, doctors and police officers will not involuntarily hold someone unless they are considered a lethal danger to self or others; that is, they have to threaten their own life or someone else's, either in words or deeds.

The duration of an involuntary hold varies. In most jurisdictions, a first hold can be no more than three to five days. But, as soon as patients demonstrate relative mental health—meaning they no longer seem to be a lethal danger to self or others—they must be released. This often happens within 24 hours.

Laws vary, but patients who do not demonstrate that they are safe can be legally held for longer periods of time. This is determined by qualified clinicians, not the patient's parents. Similarly, jurisdictions vary but, in most states, authorities can require involuntary inpatient commitment when rigorous legal standards are met.

Aftercare

Any inpatient treatment protocol should incorporate aftercare plans in order to facilitate a smooth transition to home. Some states even require a comprehensive discharge plan for pediatric psychiatric patients. The treatment facility should send you and your child home with an aftercare strategy that includes a well-defined plan describing your child's need for supervision, special education, medication, and aftercare service. This might include appointments with your child's doctor and other providers or it might involve outpatient treatment in a day facility. If needed, the facility should give you a list of organizations, facilities, and individuals who are available to provide the recommended services, and an evaluation of your child's potential eligibility for public benefits such as public assistance, Medicaid, and Supplemental Security Income.

Understand that this can be a scary time for a young person who has struggled with a mental illness, and returning to school can be especially stressful.

Chapter 7—How to Help Your Kid

GETTING REAL: LIZ

After giving birth prematurely to triplets, Dawn was connected to resources designed to help her tiny babies thrive even before they were released from the hospital. Staff at the neonatal intensive care unit at the hospital in northern Virginia notified county health services to monitor the triplets' development.

As first-time parents, Dawn and her husband, who had conceived through in vitro fertilization, were grateful for the help, especially when it became apparent that the youngest and smallest of the three wasn't keeping up. Unlike her two brothers, Sean and Andrew, little Liz had low muscle tone and a large head she couldn't hold up. Any variation in her routine upset her an inordinate amount and she didn't like to be held.

A speech therapist who was working with the children when they were about 18 months old noticed Liz would withdraw to a corner and shake her head. The speech therapist recommended an evaluation of this atypical behavior.

A doctor who saw Liz said he could diagnose her with autism, but he wasn't a fan of labeling small children and the family was already working with the therapeutic services that could help her.

Liz and her brothers, who were especially close, continued to get an array of help from county health services through preschool. When the triplets were 2, Dawn gave birth to a girl, Emily. The triplets started kindergarten and attended grade school without special help, getting good grades. When the triplets were 8, Dawn and her husband used a surrogate to gestate one of the embryos created during their previous fertility treatments and another little girl was born into their family.

Andrew's social quirks probably place him somewhere on the autism spectrum, too, although Dawn admits she didn't want to confront a diagnosis for him while the family dealt with Liz's more serious difficulties.

Liz's struggle to make friends and keep track of details through the school day really kicked in by fifth grade. Heading off to middle school for sixth grade made it even worse. Switching classes, having different teachers and the sheer number of students overwhelmed Liz, although she didn't complain. At the end of the school year, however, she confided in her mother that she had been cutting herself to cope with the stress from school and her growing feeling that she didn't fit in. She noticed that she wasn't like her classmates and felt that people were staring at her, talking about her and giving her strange looks.

Her parents got her into therapy with a counselor, who said that Liz might have Attention Deficit Hyperactivity Disorder. Dawn felt that her daughter was making progress until about midway through seventh grade. She began to have trouble with simple daily tasks. She couldn't remember the steps to wash her hair and would repeatedly ask her mom whether the shampoo or the conditioner came first.

The counselor recommended additional psychological testing to get to the root of Liz's struggles. She was diagnosed with chronic depression, anxiety and Asperger's syndrome and started seeing a new therapist and taking Celexa, a selective serotonin reuptake inhibitor (SSRI). She stopped cutting herself.

Always artistic, Liz's creativity bloomed and she wrote regularly, getting permission to use the family computer and pouring out her heart. Her subjects were often dark, but Dawn loved the creative way she used words.

Having wings and flying away were common themes, but Dawn started to worry that Liz's fantasies weren't harmless daydreams. Still close at an age when moms and teenage daughters often clash, the pair talked about dreams of flying and how leaving doesn't solve problems. Dawn hoped the discussions would keep her daughter grounded in reality and prevent her from drifting into dangerous delusions.

In the fall as Liz entered eighth grade, Dawn came across a death wish Liz had written, complete with a list of ideas how she could die. They discussed it at Liz's regularly scheduled therapy appointment the next day, and the therapist directed them immediately to the emergency room for a psychiatric evaluation.

Liz was admitted to a hospital two hours from the family's home. Dawn stayed with her.

The stress on Dawn was particularly high. She and her husband had just that week started meeting with a mediator to work out a legal separation that would lead to divorce. He cared for their other four children while Dawn, struggling with anger and worry over the challenges facing the family, slept on a cot in her daughter's hospital room, which reminded her of a jail cell.

But if Dawn found the psychiatric ward's private rooms clustered around a common area, unsettling and even sort of creepy, Liz settled right in. She greeted and mingled with the other kids.

A therapist explained to her shocked mother that young patients often feel relief at being around others who also have mental health struggles and are able to let their guard down. Liz was hospitalized for two weeks and switched to Zoloft, another SSRI. When she returned to home and resumed school, teachers, counselors and the vice principal helped adjust her classes to find what worked for her. They provided her with an educational assistant in a particularly stressful math class where she had trouble staying on task.

One December morning, the family was having a casual day lounging around the house in pajamas. Liz played video games while her youngest sister watched a movie. The children's father, who had set up an apartment in the basement as part of the separation, was away for the weekend.

The mellow morning shattered when Dawn went downstairs to get another movie for her youngest and saw Liz, wearing her father's letter jacket from high school, standing beneath a weight lifting apparatus. A chain from other home gym equipment was wrapped around her neck and hooked over the top of the sturdy metal structure.

Dawn screamed.

Shocked and confused by what she saw, Dawn didn't know if Liz had a fatal plan or was just experimenting. She still doesn't know what would have happened if her daughter had picked up her feet or leaned forward in a dream of flying.

The teen was admitted to a different psychiatric hospital for a week. She underwent additional testing to try to pin down whether her deep worries were her anxiety or signs of paranoia. She switched to Prozac and continued therapy, although she grumbled that her medication didn't help.

Her mother, though, believes things calmed for the 15-year-old. She and her dad are working on their relationship. She still loves long talks about progressive topics such as gay rights with her brother Sean. Her other brother, a conservative young Republican, sometimes struggles to connect with her, calling her weird.

Dawn strives to help Liz realize that after adolescence and its drive for conformity, more people will recognize the beauty of an outsider who thinks differently.

Dawn says she wants all her children to know they are valued for who they are. She makes sure she has one-on-one time with each child, taking time to talk with them as she shuttles them between school and activities, making sure they are coping with the complexities of life.

She also draws strength from a close relationship with her dad, talking daily on the phone, and from her faith and her friends at church. She's found support from friends going through similar situations: both her separation and her child's mental illness.

Through it all, Dawn says she has maintained her natural optimism and grown more compassionate as she has learned to navigate the mental health system and advocate for her child.

"Normal" children may be stubborn, angry, wild, quirky, or spirited—and they might be whatever way they are because they are exceptionally creative or highly sensitive or some other aspect of their personality or nature makes them a unique individual. Or, they might have ADHD, autism, PTSD, oppositional defiant disorder, a learning disability, a mood disorder, or something else.

You may be concerned about your child's behavior—and you may address it with your family pediatrician and perhaps a specialist—but, meanwhile, you still have the job of parenting your child, and this can be hard. Of course, more books and websites than any parent can read are available with advice, tips, and programs, and nearly one-thousand books on the market provide strategies on how to deal with "spirited" children. If you're the parent of a difficult child, many of these will help.

Most experts recommend that parents accept their child for who they are, and learn ways to channel a child's strengths. This might be validation as you honor and embrace your child's idiosyncrasies and natural gifts, or it might be an "opposite influence," such as a calm friend for an amped-up child.[11] Experts also encourage parents to establish clear rules with consequences and rewards.

Limit Setting

Limit setting—easier said than done, right? For years, our family was in constant crisis with Chloe and it was all we could do to survive and not trigger another rage or explosion. It was exhausting and most other extended family, friends and school staff really didn't get what was going on in our house and typically placed blame or gave "tough love" suggestions.

What was critical for Jeff and I was to establish what was NOT acceptable in our house and if Chloe crossed the line, we would call the police. Below are behaviors that we did not tolerate from Chloe, especially as she got older and was more difficult for me to contain and her sister to handle.

Behaviors That Should NOT Be Tolerated:

- Physical abuse.
- Sexual abuse.
- Destruction of property.
- Setting fires or creating fire hazards.
- Stealing.
- Illegal alcohol or drug use.
- Severely disruptive or tyrannical behaviors.

What you can expect from your mentally ill child and one that's recovering from a relapse is diminished abilities with normal daily living. Again, it's important to recognize that they have an illness and may never be able to perform at the level or expectation of other family members.

The most helpful reminders Jeff and I say to each other are, "Pick your battles" and "It is what it is." Once you start accepting your child for who they are, many of the areas that drove you crazy before, don't seem that important any more. What we deem as important for Chloe is that she's mentally and physically healthy, learning and maintaining boundaries, and learning values and morals.

Below outlines behaviors and symptoms that might be present in your ill or relapsing child, as well as behaviors you expect from a healthy child. Trying to change any of the behaviors of a mentally ill child is like trying to tell a diabetic they don't need their insulin. The behaviors are due to a chemical imbalance in the brain that the child CANNOT control.

Behaviors which may be a result of mental illness	Behaviors you expect from a healthy child
Constant tension and nervousness	Ability to focus and concentrate
Irritability, criticalness, even abusiveness	Insight about what is happening
Unpredictable over-reaction to things	Pride in appearance and personal hygiene
Indifference; inflexible obstinacy	Capacity for intimacy
Irrational statements and responses	Ability to cope with minor problems
Obsession with own activities and pursuits; inflated self-concept	Optimism, faith, belief in the future
Forgetfulness and losing things	Warmth and thoughtfulness in relationships
Uncontrollable sadness or crying	Ability to appreciate people and accept their help
Rudeness and hostility	Pride in taking responsibility
Fearfulness and hyper-vigilance	Ability to express joy
Devastated by peer disapproval	Capacity to see another point of view
Disinterest in sex, or hypersexuality	Emotional resiliency
Indecisiveness	Willingness to follow treatment plan when ill
Inappropriate and bizarre behaviors	
Wish to be withdrawn and isolated	

Parenting Styles

Psychologists today recognize four major parenting styles: hands-off (also known as "neglectful"), permissive, authoritarian, and authoritative. With distinct characteristics, each style results in specific responses in children, although parents and children vary as much as these relationships do.[12]

Hands-Off Parenting

Hands-off parenting is also known as neglectful parenting, as hands-off parents do not care for their children's emotional or physical needs. They don't know what their children are up to, who their friends are, or how their children are doing in school. These parents may spend little time at home with children, often making excuses for their absence, and are not involved in school, sports, play dates, or the child's life, at home or away.

A harmful parenting style, this can be damaging to children. With little parental feedback, such children do not develop a trust foundation with their parents so they have a hard time forming relationships with other people, particularly their peers. To get these families back on track, parents who tend toward neglectful parenting can readily improve through intervention, education, and the direction of a family doctor or therapist.

Permissive or Indulgent Parenting

These parents are responsive to their children, and very nurturing and loving, but they tend to be too lenient. Trying to avoid confrontation, these parents set few rules and then apply them inconsistently to avoid conflict or to accommodate a child's mood. As a result of too much freedom without consequences, these children have a lack of structure and, therefore, little self-discipline or self-control.

Children feel safe when given a sense of structure, understanding of consequences, and expectations of the clear roles and boundaries for both parent and child. Without providing that structure, permissive or indulgent parenting is unhealthy and potentially damaging as children of such parents can experience insecurity, poor social skills, self-centeredness, lack of motivation, and problems with authority figures.

Some parents are just afraid to upset their children while others may adopt an indulgent parenting style as an extreme opposite approach to their own experience growing up with authoritarian parents. While remaining loving and responsive, permissive parents need to learn to set boundaries and rules for their children or, if they can't seem to accomplish this, to seek the help of a therapist.

Authoritarian or Strict Parenting

Authoritarian parents provide a lot of structure and expect their children to follow a strict set of rules and expectations without much exception and without much dialogue or explanation. In these families, punishment is the parents' go-to method of getting results, while nurturing is reserved. Children of such parents have few choices and they make few decisions. These parents do not balance all their emphasis on structure with open communication to help their children understand the reasons for the rules. These children can end up with low self-esteem and social problems, such as becoming fearful or shy, or misbehaving when their parents aren't around, and they might confuse obedience with love. If authoritarian parents find it too hard to open communication with their child, a therapist can help.

Authoritative Parenting

Authoritative parenting is widely regarded as the healthiest parenting style. These parents have set high standards and clear structure for their children, but this is balanced by parental understanding and support for children, as well. Helping to foster a productive relationship between parent and child, this parenting style includes a reasonable and clear structure and routine—such as a regular bedtime and house rules—along with a good understanding and open communication between parents and children. These children understand the expectations and consequences and feel that they can speak openly to their parents without fear of consequences, judgment, or reprimand. As parents nurture this open communication, they will help their children to grapple with the ups and downs and decisions of their own lives.

Although an authoritative parent can generally maintain a healthy household, parents and kids obviously vary—infinitely. And, as parents, we always have to adapt and adjust to changing circumstances, personalities, and needs. What's more, as parents of children who have behavioral problems or disorders, we have to adapt and adjust a lot. As always, therapists or counselors can provide great help for parents who feel overwhelmed.

Tips that Actually Work with Difficult Kids

Though it may feel like it, you are not alone in learning how to parent a child with mental illness. Many resources are available to you and your family as you navigate these new challenges. Remember that it is important that you not neglect yourself; be sure to see my chapter on Caring for Yourself and Your Family.

In terms of helping your mentally ill child, the first real hurdle is to come to terms with the fact that you and your family are in a "new normal." This can be a long and hard process but, as parents, we need to realize that a child who has a mental health condition may never be the same. Our dreams and plans for the future may have to evolve, along with our household rules and other daily routines. If we don't realize and accept a child's limitations, we will constantly run up against frustration, stress, and—probably—defeat.

Given the expectations of an effective, authoritative parent, we need to keep a few things in mind when it comes to parenting a child who is dealing with mental illness. While you still need to establish your household expectations and structure, you might need to consider your child's mental health as you set those expectations. If you can learn to accept what your child can and cannot control, you can adjust your own attitude about success and failure. This will help you to be less angry or disappointed over problematic behaviors and, in turn, to learn to remain respectful and understanding of your child's feelings— even when everything seems to be working against you.[13]

HALT! A Tried and True Method for Managing Emotions

HALT is a great technique for anyone to use to manage emotions and moods, but it's especially useful for those who are dealing with mental illness. The HALT Method suggests that people are healthier and function better if they never get too:

- Hungry
- Angry
- Lonely
- Tired

Even if you are mentally healthy, ignoring any of these conditions for too long can really affect your mood. But, for your child or anyone with a mental illness, managing HALT is critical to avoiding major relapses and keeping a healthy balance in life.

Hungry. As you probably know, the food you eat can have a direct effect on your energy level, physical health, and mood. When your blood level drops or spikes, it can also have a dramatic impact on mental stability. Experts agree that regular meals and snacks that combine a protein with a nutrient-dense carbohydrate and healthy fat are the key to a balanced diet and mind. For those who struggle with depression, some vitamins and minerals—folate, vitamin B12, calcium, iron, selenium, zinc and omega-3—may help with symptoms.

Angry. Anger is a normal human emotion that can cause anything from slight irritation to strong rage. But suppressed anger can be an underlying cause of anxiety and depression, which can disrupt thinking and behavior patterns and even cause physical health problems. If you find anger to be a problem, these techniques can help you manage anger and stress:

- Calm and center yourself by practicing deep belly breathing.
- Use positive words like "relax" or "slow down" in self-talk to counter angry thoughts.
- If you have issues with someone, be calm, assertive, and direct instead of aggressive.
- Seek out support and talk through your feelings.
- Keep a log of when you feel angry so you can spot any patterns.

- Use empathy to put yourself in someone else's place.
- Learn to laugh at yourself.
- If your anger is affecting your relationships or health, seek professional help.

Lonely. Everyone feels lonely from time to time, but long periods of loneliness or social isolation can negatively impact your health as much as obesity does. Studies show that loneliness increases the risk for death by 45% and the chance of developing dementia by 64%. Research also suggests that people need to attend to loneliness just as they would their diet, exercise, or sleep. So, what should a lonely person do?

- Recognize your loneliness.
- Understand what loneliness is doing to your mind and body, so you are motivated to do something about it.
- Respond to your loneliness "safely." Social media isn't a substitute for face-to-face contact, but it's better than nothing. Although you may be nervous or self-conscious at first, it's best to join something that's a bit outside your comfort zone. It's usually worth it.
- If loneliness comes with anxiety or depression, a therapist can help.

Tired. Sleep is critical to good mental health! To think clearly and keep moods in check, everyone needs a good night sleep. But, for someone managing a mental illness, sleep deprivation can trigger depression, manic episodes, and psychosis. For anyone struggling with falling asleep or staying asleep, these tips might help:

- Go to bed at the same time every night and get up at the same time every morning.
- Establish a bedtime ritual.
- Avoid caffeine after 1 PM.
- Eat on a regular schedule and avoid heavy meals before bedtime.
- Exercise daily but avoid strenuous exercise right before bedtime.
- Play soothing music or read.
- Take a warm bath or shower.
- Place lavender oil on your pillow or by your bedside.

- Consult a health care provider if you have more serious sleep challenges.

Collaborative and Proactive Solutions

Child psychologist Ross Greene, PhD, developed a groundbreaking approach to working with difficult kids. In my experience, I have found it amazing that a change in approach and wording with challenging youth can produce enlightening and mutually agreeable conversations. That's right: I said "enlightening and agreeable conversations" and "challenging youth" in the same sentence.

Let me be clear... This strategy doesn't make miracles happen and it's also not easy. But, if you use it, practice it, and refine it, it's about one-thousand percent better than the alternative, which is living in crisis day in and day out while you scream and your child rages.

Dr. Greene's program is called Collaborative and Proactive Solutions.[14] His assertion—and mine—is that children *do not intentionally want to behave badly*. In fact, they want to do well. This goes for all children, difficult or otherwise. Greene says that children respond with challenging behavior when the demands of the environment exceed the kid's capacity to respond adaptively. In other words, he says, kids are challenging because *they lack the skills not to be challenging*. "...Your first goal is to identify the skills that are lagging in the kid you're trying to understand and help," says Dr. Greene. "Your second goal is to identify the specific conditions (these are called 'unsolved problems') in which challenging behavior is occurring." If we can identify the lagging skills and the problems they cause, we can work with kids to create solutions together.

Instead of focusing on behavior, we should focus on any lagging skills and then create a plan to solve any underlying problems. Hence, the name Collaborative and Proactive Solutions.

In order to solve problems collaboratively and proactively with our kids, we need to understand the specific problems that they're dealing with. Then we can work with the child to solve those problems while simultaneously teaching the child the skills he or she is lacking.

The following is an abbreviated version of Dr. Greene's comprehensive method, which includes step-by-step worksheets and complete information on how to use the strategy most effectively. See the resources at the back of this book for more information.

- **Use empathy.** Using empathy with your challenging child goes a long way in breaking down barriers and encouraging open communication, but for many parents and authority figures this can be a difficult mindset to change.

  After you express your observation and ask an open-ended question about it, be quiet. Let them talk—and listen to them. If they respond with a shoulder shrug or "I don't know," offer some suggestions. "Are you having trouble with a class? Is it hard to do your homework right after a long day at school?" Again, zip it and see what your child says. You'll be amazed at what you learn.

Instead of scolding...	Ask what's up...
"Do as you're told."	"What's going on? Are you okay?"
"It's 10 PM and you haven't even started your homework! What's wrong with you? Why can't you just come home and get it done after school?!"	"Hey, so... I noticed that you've been having difficulty getting your homework done. What's the deal?"
"Stop screaming at the dog! He's just drinking his water. You have to drink too, right!?"	"It seems like you've been getting really upset with the dog when he drinks his water. What's up?"

- **Let them know that you heard their concerns.** After your child tells you what's up, repeat back what you heard. Then validate your understanding by asking your child, "Is that right? Is there anything else?" Work on this until you are confident that you understand your child's real concerns. For example:

"So, you said after a long day of school the last thing you want to do is homework. You want to relax and play video games but all I do is nag you. Plus, your math class is really hard and you're getting behind in it. Is that about right?"

"You say that, when the dog drinks his water, it really bothers your ears... Are there other things that bother your ears?"

- Brainstorm solutions. Work with your child to find solutions that will help solve the problem or alleviate their difficulties with it.

"You know, Dad is really good at math and I know he'd be happy to help you get back on track. Would that be okay?"

"What about the homework thing? What would help you get started on it?"

"Okay, so would it be okay if I set a timer or let you know when you've been home for more than an hour?"

"What if we move the dog's drinking water to another room? Do you think that would help?"

"If noisy kids bother you in school, maybe we could talk to your teacher about moving you to a quieter table. Would that be a good idea?"

Other soothing techniques that work for some parents include:

- Water – whether it's putting a bowl of water with a dropper in front of a child, swimming or taking a bath with bubbles, water is often very soothing for anxious children
- Putty or playdough
- Yoga balls
- Therapy swing
- Soft or fuzzy blanket or cloth
- Music and/or sound-cancelling headphones
- Gently patting or squeezing the child's shoulders and head

As you utilize this method with your child, keep in mind that it will be an ongoing process that will take continuous effort—by you and your child. It may go more smoothly at times and not so well at other times, and it will never be perfect—but it will help. Be gentle and forgiving with your child and yourself. From my own experience with Chloe, I promise that you will gain a better understanding of your child's concerns, fears, and struggles. Through that understanding, you can establish a closer bond and relationship, which is always a good thing.

Effective Communication Strategies

Dr. Greene's method has also been used with our family while Chloe has been in residential treatment. You can learn more about the model at Dr. Greene's website, www.livesinthebalance.org, as well as books and resources for parents. Below are some quick, effective communication strategies to try with your child.

- ▶ **Ask open-ended questions:** "What's going on? You seem upset" (insert emotion)...(recognize they are having a difficult time)
- ▶ **Don't criticize.** People struggling with any sort of mental illness are very vulnerable and cannot defend themselves against direct personal attack. Try to be supportive and keep negative or nagging remarks to an absolute minimum. If there is one single standard to work for in your relationship with your youth, it is to respect and protect their shattered self-esteem.
- ▶ **Don't press; don't fight; don't punish.**
- ▶ **Praise positive behavior every chance you get.** Study after study shows that if you "accentuate the positive" people will want to perform the behaviors that earn them recognition and approval. Many reliable studies indicate that criticism, conflict and emotional pressure are most highly related to relapse.
- ▶ **Learn to recognize and accept the primary symptoms and the residual symptoms of your youth's mental illness.** Don't try to "jump start" someone in a depression or "shoot down" a person with mania. Help them learn which of their behaviors are caused by their illness. Tell them it's not their fault if they cannot get out of a depression, that they are not "terrible" for the things they did when they were manic, etc. This kind of support relieves a lot of guilt and anxiety, even when someone is still in denial.
- ▶ **Don't buy into the stigma all around you.** People with mental illness are not "bad" or ill because of some failure of character. Your child is not willfully trying to disgrace you, frustrate you and embarrass you. Their behavior is not a reflection on your relationship or your parenting. They are not dedicated to undermining your dignity or ruining your prestige and standing in the community. They are simply ill. Stigma is awfully hard to bear in mental illness, but we certainly don't have to go along with it!
- ▶ **Lessen your demand for support from your ill youth.** People with mental illness become very "self" involved when so much of their ...

152

identity and self-respect is at stake. They often cannot fulfill normal family roles. Seek additional sources of emotional support for yourself when there is mental illness in the family. Then your child can be who they are, and they will feel less guilty for letting you down.

▶ **Having made these necessary allowances, treat your youth with mental illness, day-to-day, just like anybody else.** Expect the "basics" your family requires to get along together, and set the same limits and expectations for reasonable order that would exist if they were well. It is very reassuring to people with mental illness when there is a clear distinction between them as a person and them as someone who has a problem with disordered behavior. Everyone requires rules of conduct and cooperative standards to live by.

▶ **It is important to encourage independent behavior.** Communicate with your child what they feel ready to do. Plan for progress in small steps that have a better chance for success. Make short-term plans and goals and be prepared for changes in directions, and retreats. Progress in mental illness requires flexibility; it means giving up your zeal for progress measured by normal standards. There is lots more danger in pushing than there is in waiting. When they are ready, they will move.

▶ **It doesn't help to cling to the past, or dwell on "what might have been."** The best gift we can offer our child is to accept that their mental illness is a fact and part of your life. It is important to tell your youth that mental illness makes life difficult, but not impossible. Communicate that most people with a mental illness do struggle but are able to build lives.

▶ **Every time your child "gets better" and shows improvement, for them it means that they are moving back into risk position.** Being well signals that they might be required to participate in the real world, and this is a frightening prospect for the "shaky self." So, it's important for you to be very patient in wellness, just as you try to be in illness. People recovering from mental illness still have the awesome task of accepting what has happened to them, finding new meaning in life and constructing a way of living that protects them from becoming ill again.

▶ **Empathy must also extend to yourself,** who struggles to understand and encourage your child who has a mental illness. Remember: You can only try to do your best. Some illness processes can get "stuck" no matter what you do to help. Brain disorders go through hard, intractable periods where helping those who suffer them is often very difficult to do. We can hope, we can assist, we can keep trying, ...

Effective Communication Strategies (cont.)

but we can't produce miracles.

▶ The most important "grace" one learns in the process of caring for someone with a mental illness is tolerance, charity, endurance and self-restraint. Do not criticize yourself if you sometimes cannot muster up these graces when you are feeling frightened or frustrated. Coming to terms with changed life circumstances with any serious illness is a huge adjustment. Your empathetic understanding will deepen and enrich your relationships with your youth who suffers from a mental illness.

Chapter 8—The Trouble with School

GETTING REAL: REBECCA

Diane knew well by then that Rebecca was troubled. She'd grown from an infant who did everything more slowly than her peers to a toddler incapable of playing on her own to a preschooler who sat in her car seat, staring straight ahead while her mother attempted to interest her in the world. When Rebecca did engage, it was often with a wild rush of adrenaline or violent emotional outbursts that left everyone exhausted.

In school, Rebecca quickly fell behind her classmates. Teachers understood something was up but moved her through the grades, assuring Diane that her striking, social, normal-appearing daughter was easily distracted but would soon catch up. But by the end of fifth grade, her friends were reading Harry Potter while Rebecca still struggled through picture books. Athletic by nature, she joined a soccer team but couldn't coordinate herself enough to connect with the ball. Friendships became difficult as it became more obvious that Rebecca was different.

As Rebecca started middle school, Diane's growing frustration with the school system reached a peak. As a student, Rebecca was far behind academically and struggling socially, and Diane knew that the school would not take time to understand her daughter. Rebecca's teachers told Diane they thought she was lazy. At one point, Diane hired a lawyer, thinking she'd sue to get her daughter the attention she needed. The lawyer declined the case after she saw Rebecca; a judge would never believe such a normal-looking girl was so troubled, she said.

Rebecca spent her final year of middle school in an outdoor education program that seemed to help. Then, Rebecca's therapist diagnosed her with bipolar disorder. Armed with the diagnosis, Diane enrolled Rebecca in a wilderness therapy program for troubled kids, and the staff soon recognized that Rebecca was struggling with learning disabilities. They brought in a psychologist who tested Rebecca and gave Diane a 20-page report that she used to guide the remainder of her daughter's high school education.

Still, those years were not smooth. Rebecca returned home and enrolled in her local high school only to struggle again, reading at a second-grade level and doing math at a first-grade level. The summer after her sophomore year, her mother sent her to an out-of-state residential high school for developmentally disabled teens.

The skill of the staff worked wonders for the teen, who returned home the following spring with academic skills that were nearly appropriate for her grade level. Her mother re-enrolled her in public school. But instead of keeping up with her peers, Rebecca turned to partying with new friends. Three months after she returned, she overdosed on marijuana laced with bath salts and landed in the hospital emergency room, near death. The overdose jumbled Rebecca's speech for several days and sent her into a full-blown psychosis. Her high school career was over.

––––––––––––

Why Does Mental Health Matter in Schools?

Addressing mental health needs in school is critically important because 1 in 5 children and youth have a diagnosable emotional, behavioral or mental health disorder and 1 in 10 young people have a mental health challenge that is severe enough to impair how they function at home, school or in the community.[15]

Many estimates show that even though mental illness affects so many of our kids aged 6-17 at least one-half and many estimate as many as 80% of them do not receive the mental health care they need.

Being able to recognize and support kids' mental health in schools matters because:

- Mental health problems are common and often develop during childhood and adolescence
- They are treatable!
- Early detection and intervention strategies work. They can help improve resilience and the ability to succeed in school & life.

In addition, youth with emotional and behavioral disorders have the worst graduation rate of all students with disabilities. Nationally, only 40% of students with emotional, behavioral and mental health disorders graduate from high school, compared to the national average of 76%; and, over 50% of students with emotional and behavioral disabilities ages 14 and older, drop out of high school. This is the highest dropout rate of any disability group!

Navigating School and Mental Health

Without assistance, children with mental health conditions may struggle in school, and these challenges will likely cause extra frustration and stress. Depending on the state and resources, school districts vary on the level of support they provide to mentally challenged kids. Over the course of Chloe's treatment, I've learned many school districts across the country will only provide the minimum support they can get away with, not necessarily what's required by law. The reasons may range from lack of knowledge to strained resources but the reality is many students do not receive the resources they need to succeed in school.

Disabilities Covered Under Section 504

By law, the U.S. Department of Education enforces Section 504 in programs and activities that receive financial assistance from the Department of Ed.

The ED Section 504 regulation defines an "individual with handicaps" as any person who (i) has a physical or mental impairment which substantially limits one or more major life activities, (ii) has a record of such an impairment, or (iii) is regarded as having such an impairment. The regulation further defines a physical or mental impairment as (A) any physiological disorder or condition, cosmetic disfigurement, or anatomical loss affecting one or more of the following body systems: neurological; musculoskeletal; special sense organs; respiratory, including speech organs; cardiovascular; reproductive; digestive; genitourinary; hemic and lymphatic; skin; and endocrine; or (B) any mental or psychological disorder, such as mental retardation, organic brain syndrome, emotional or mental illness, and specific learning disabilities. The definition does not set forth a list of specific diseases and conditions that constitute physical or mental impairments because of the difficulty of ensuring the comprehensiveness of any such list.

The key factor in determining whether a person is considered an "individual with handicaps" covered by Section 504 is whether the physical or mental impairment results in a substantial limitation of one or more major life activities. Major life activities, as defined in the regulation, include functions such as caring for one's self, performing manual tasks, walking, seeing, hearing, speaking, breathing, learning, and working.

The impairment must have a material effect on one's ability to perform a major life activity. For example, an individual who has a physical or mental impairment would not be considered a person with handicaps if the condition does not in any way limit the individual, or only results in some minor limitation. However, in some cases Section 504 also protects individuals who do not have a handicapping condition but are treated as though they do because they have a history of, or have been misclassified as having, a mental or physical impairment that substantially limits one or more major life activities. For example, if you have a history of a handicapping condition but no longer have the condition, or have been incorrectly classified as having such a condition, you too are protected from discrimination under Section 504. Frequently occurring examples of the first group are persons with histories of mental or emotional illness, heart disease, or cancer; of the second group, persons who have been misclassified as mentally retarded. Persons who are not disabled may be covered by Section

504 also if they are treated as if they are handicapped, for example, if they are infected with the human immunodeficiency virus.

What Are Hidden Disabilities?

Hidden disabilities are physical or mental impairments that are not readily apparent to others. They include such conditions and diseases as specific learning disabilities, diabetes, epilepsy, and allergy. A disability such as a limp, paralysis, total blindness or deafness is usually obvious to others. But hidden disabilities such as low vision, poor hearing, heart disease, or chronic illness may not be obvious. A chronic illness involves a recurring and long-term disability such as diabetes, heart disease, kidney and liver disease, high blood pressure, or ulcers.

Approximately four million students with disabilities are enrolled in public elementary and secondary schools in the United States. Of these, 43 % are students classified as learning disabled, 8 % as emotionally disturbed, and 1 % as other health impaired. These hidden disabilities often cannot be readily known without the administration of appropriate diagnostic tests.

The Responsibilities of ED Recipients in Preschool, Elementary, Secondary, and Adult Education

For coverage under Section 504, an individual with handicaps must be "qualified" for service by the school or institution receiving ED funds. For example, the ED Section 504 regulation defines a "qualified handicapped person" with respect to public preschool, elementary, secondary, or adult education services, as a person with a handicap who is:

- of an age during which persons without handicaps are provided such services;
- of any age during which it is mandatory under state law to provide such services to persons with handicaps; or
- a person for whom a state is required to provide a free appropriate public education under the Individuals with Disabilities Education Act.

Under the Section 504 regulation, a recipient that operates a public elementary or secondary education program has a number of responsibilities toward qualified handicapped persons in its jurisdiction. These recipients must:

- Undertake annually to identify and locate all unserved handicapped children;
- Provide a "free appropriate public education" to each student with handicaps, regardless of the nature or severity of the handicap. This means providing regular or special education and related aids and services designed to meet the individual educational needs of handicapped persons as adequately as the needs of nonhandicapped persons are met;
- Ensure that each student with handicaps is educated with non-handicapped students to the maximum extent appropriate to the needs of the handicapped person;
- Establish nondiscriminatory evaluation and placement procedures to avoid the inappropriate education that may result from the misclassification or misplacement of students;
- Establish procedural safeguards to enable parents and guardians to participate meaningfully in decisions regarding the evaluation and placement of their children; and
- Afford handicapped children an equal opportunity to participate in nonacademic and extracurricular services and activities.

A recipient that operates a preschool education or day care program or an adult education program may not exclude qualified handicapped persons and must take into account their needs of qualified handicapped persons in determining the aid, benefits, or services to be provided under those programs and activities.

Students with hidden disabilities frequently are not properly diagnosed. For example, a student with an undiagnosed hearing impairment may be unable to understand much of what a teacher says; a student with a learning disability may be unable to process oral or written information routinely; or a student with an emotional problem may be unable to concentrate in a regular classroom setting. As a result, these students, regardless of their intelligence, will be unable to fully demonstrate their ability or attain educational benefits equal to that of non-handicapped students. They may be perceived by teachers and fellow students as slow, lazy, or as discipline problems.

Whether a child is already in school or not, if his/her parents feel the child needs special education or related services, they should get in touch with the local superintendent of schools. For example, a parent who believes his or her child has a hearing impairment or is having difficulty understanding a teacher may request to have the child evaluated so that the child may receive appropriate education. A child with behavior problems, or one who is doing poorly academically, may have an undiagnosed hidden disability. A parent has the right to request that the school determine whether the child is handicapped and whether special education or related services are needed to provide the child an appropriate education. Once it is determined that a child needs special education or related services, the recipient school system must arrange to provide appropriate services.

How Can the Needs of Students with Hidden Disabilities Be Addressed?

As we've said about treatment plans for children and youth with mental illnesses, so education might need tailoring to the specific child's disabilities or combination of disabilities, especially when concurrent hidden disabilities may be represented. The following are examples to illustrate how schools can address the needs of their students with hidden disabilities:

- A student with a long-term, debilitating medical problem such as cancer, kidney disease, or diabetes may be given special consideration to accommodate the student's needs. For example, a student with cancer may need a class schedule that allows for rest and recuperation following chemotherapy.
- A student with a learning disability that affects the ability to demonstrate knowledge on a standardized test or in certain testing situations may require modified test arrangements, such as oral testing or different testing formats.
- A student with a learning disability or impaired vision that affects the ability to take notes in class may need a notetaker or tape recorder.

- A student with a chronic medical problem such as kidney or liver disease may have difficulty in walking distances or climbing stairs. Under Section 504, this student may require special parking space, sufficient time between classes, or other considerations to conserve the student's energy for academic pursuits.
- A student with diabetes, which adversely affects the body's ability to manufacture insulin, may need a class schedule that will accommodate the student's special needs for blood sugar monitoring or insulin injections.
- An emotionally or mentally ill student may need an adjusted class schedule to allow time for regular counseling or therapy.
- A student with epilepsy who has no control over seizures, and whose seizures are stimulated by stress or tension, may need accommodation for such stressful activities as lengthy academic testing or competitive endeavors in physical education.
- A student with arthritis may have persistent pain, tenderness or swelling in one or more joints. A student experiencing arthritic pain may require a modified physical education program or modified seating in the classroom.

These are just a few examples of how the needs of students with hidden disabilities may be addressed. If you are a student (or a parent or guardian of a student) with a hidden disability, or represent an institution seeking to address the needs of such students, you may wish to seek further information from OCR.

Developing an Individualized Education Plan

An Individualized Education Plan (IEP) is the plan of services and supports that will help your child to learn and be successful at school. This plan will be created by your IEP Team which will include a number of people including you, your child (if appropriate), a special education teacher, a general education teacher, a school representative qualified to provide or supervise special education programs and one who is knowledgeable about curriculum and public resources; a member of the Multidisciplinary Evaluation Team (if this is an initial IEP) and a school psychologist or someone who is able to interpret the evaluation results.

After eligibility is established, the team must consider a variety of things as they work to create the plan, including: your child's strengths, your concerns as a parent, the results of the evaluations, and, your child's academic, behavioral, social, functional and communication needs.

After discussing your child's needs in all of the above areas, the team will create a Present Level of Academic Achievement and Functional Performance (P.L.A.A.F.P.) statement, which will describe how your child is doing right now.

The PLAAFP statement should list your child's strengths, needs and include a description of how your child is doing in comparison to his or her peers, grade level expectations and age-appropriate developmental and behavioral skills. It should also address all areas of development where your child may need support, including academic, behavioral, social, communication, sensory and daily living skills. It should describe how your child's disability affects his or his involvement in the general education curriculum and school's activities, as well as its effect on your child's ability to learn and do the types of things that other kids of their same age can do. The PLAAFP statement should describe the strategies and supports that help your child to learn and the things that interfere with their success. It should also include information from their most current evaluations.

The PLAAFP statement is very important! The information within it is used to help develop goals and objectives for your child. It will also help the team identify the specific services and supports including special education, accommodations and modifications (things your child may need to help them be successful in the classroom like changes to instruction, materials, the classroom environment) and supplementary services (aids, technology, services or supports for school personnel) your child may need in order to be successful.

The next task of the IEP team will be to develop goals for your child to meet over the next year. Goals are written statements that describe what the student will learn, what skills they will gain, or what they will focus on for the next year. Each concern identified in the PLAAFP statement should have a corresponding goal to address it.

IEP goals and objectives should address all areas of need for your child, including academics, social needs, behavioral or organizational concerns, and communication needs. Remember goals are based on individual needs and can be created to help with difficulties with learning, social interactions; strategies to recognize and address anxiety, opposition, impulsivity, social skills, staying on tasks, etc.

These goals are very important as they 'drive' the focus of special education services and supports and decide specifically how your child will benefit from special education. The goals described in your child's IEP should be very clear, concrete, and well defined. You should be able to easily recognize when your child is making progress. Your child's school will measure your child's progress toward these goals and will provide you with written progress reports right along with your regular report card.

Questions you might want to ask about the goals created for your child:

- Is the goal tied to my child's participation in or progression in the general curriculum?
- Will it help my child to benefit from or participate in instruction or classroom interactions?
- Is it reasonable as well as challenging?

After creating goals and deciding which services and supports are necessary to meet your child's needs and reach those goals, the IEP team will then discuss where your child will receive these services.

Your child's school is required to provide special education services in the "least restrictive environment (LRE), which means that your child will spend as much time as possible learning in regular education classes with his or her classmates at your home school. If possible the school will provide the services your child needs within the school setting. If all of your child's needs cannot be met in that setting they will inform you about other options. Once the plan is complete the school will begin to implement the services and supports for your child.

At least once a year your child's IEP team will sit down together and review the IEP, your child's progress toward their goals and make any changes that are necessary.

Addressing Behavioral Issues in Your Child's IEP

If your child struggles with behavioral issues in school, you may want to request a Functional Behavioral Assessment and Positive Behavioral Supports. It is important to keep in mind that behavior is often a form of communication and is used to get something, control something, or escape something.

Before you begin to create positive behavior support plan or goals it is often helpful to get a solid behavioral evaluation with recommendations. Functional Behavior Assessments are evaluations and observations that seek to understand the child's behaviors and why they do what they do. They also look at the interaction between a child and their environment. After a series of observations, the evaluator can create an informed hypothesis (or best guess) of why they think the behavior is occurring and then this information can be used to help create goals to try to positively change behavior.

Creating Successful Positive Behavior Support Plans

One important thing to keep in mind is that positive behavior support plans are not discipline plans. The basis for creating a Positive Behavior Intervention Plan should be focused on teaching new behaviors and skills and should also include the instruction and assistance needed to help the student to use and practice the skills they have been taught to make better choices and have better outcomes. If you are concerned that your child's plan seems more like a discipline plan than a positive behavior support plan it may be helpful to ask what skills are being taught, practiced and reinforced. Positive behavior plans should be proactive and include planned interventions and instruction. Plans may also sometimes include modifying the environment, especially if your child has sensory or other issues that may have a negative effect on their behavior. Positive behavior interventions should be designed to change outcomes by preventing behavior from occurring, reducing the severity of the behavior, or de-escalating behavior before it becomes extreme.

When helping to create a successful behavior plan for your child, remember that your input can be critical as you know your child best!

Issues with Discipline at School Including Suspension & Expulsion

If your child is eligible for special education and/or if your child's school is aware that he or she has a disability, there are limits to the school's ability to suspend or exclude your child from school for behavior related to your child's disability. If the school wants to exclude your child for more than 10 days, the school must hold a meeting to determine whether your child's behavior was a result of their disability. If it is, then your child cannot be excluded from school unless you agree to the arrangement (or unless the situation is one involving a weapon or drugs). The team must also assess if the student's IEP was being implemented correctly and if the current behavioral plan was appropriate.

If your child's behavior is not a result of a disability, the school can exclude him or her for more than 10 days. If your child is receiving services and is excluded from school for more than 10 days the school district must continue to provide the services from their IEP. The services may however be provided in an alternative setting.

If You Have to Fight for Your Child's Rights

Unfortunately, as you know, dealing with a mental illness is often confusing and unpredictable. Compounding the issue, it's also both a hidden illness and lifelong disease. And due to the stigma and misinformation surrounding mental illness, school resources and practices are often lacking for mentally disabled children and their families.

If you feel your child's education rights are not being met as protected by Section 504, there are several steps you can take:

- If you haven't already done so, meet with the principal and teacher to address the behavior issues.
- Assess whether an Individualized Education Plan (IEP) is needed. Your child may need further testing and diagnostics to qualify.
- If after several meetings with the IEP team you still feel the school is not meeting its lawful obligation, search for an education advocate or attorney in your area to consult with.

As an advocate for your child, it can be exhausting and maddening to try to convince the schools to provide education services that they are legally bound to provide. Try to keep things in perspective and know that it may be a challenge.

Chapter 9—Your Child's Social Life, Social Media, and Social Perils

GETTING REAL: REBECCA

Rebecca was 18 years old when some new friends encouraged her to get off the lithium so she could party with them. Rebecca did. Her mother could only watch as her daughter, an adult by law, started experimenting with illegal drugs and descended more deeply into an illness she continued to deny. The next year, Rebecca lost her state-funded health insurance because she didn't understand how to reapply.

Every day, Diane lives with her deepest fear that the daughter she loves so deeply will overdose on street drugs, that she will become depressed and choose to end her life, and that she will continue to avoid treatment, allowing her disease to progress.

Social Life

Sometimes it's hard to watch your kids grow up. I've personally struggled seeing Chloe trying to build friendships. It has always been a challenge for her. I can remember even at age three her pre-school teacher telling me she didn't easily make friends and would go stand by the bunny every day during recess. Chloe continues to struggle making and keeping friends. Understanding body language and boundaries for kids and people like Chloe is a challenge at best. What comes easily and naturally for sister is a daily labyrinth for Chloe, navigating what to do or say in a multitude of situations. When framed in this context, it's easy to see why kids and people with on the Autism Spectrum get frustrated and depressed.

I used to take some of Chloe's classmates from her school to an animal rehabilitation farm where the kids earn work credit. I witnessed first-hand the growing pains she and some of the other kids experienced because of their "different" behavior. Even among those kids who ignored Chloe or shunned her, it was a stark reminder that kids do the best they can with what they have. Kids' and adults' reactions are born from preconceived notions and a lack of understanding about how to interact with those unlike us.

For children, and especially teenagers, with mental illnesses, social life can range from non-existent to a parent's worst nightmare. Like Diane, we often watch teenagers with mental illness make ill-advised choices based on the advice of people who don't understand their illness or who are caught in their own struggles. Our hope is always for good friends for our children but sometimes those friends just become bad influences.

And the challenges of normal social interaction can be nothing compared to the pressures of social media.

Social Media

With all the struggles that our daughter had with establishing friendships, Chloe's use and involvement with social media served to further destroy her self-esteem. Her neurological disabilities challenged her social abilities making it difficult for her to make and keep friends. Social media became her "friend" network and a drama nightmare. Like many kids, Chloe wasn't developing interpersonal skills and was hiding behind an artificial screen of protection. She would be attacked by peers and open fire of unimaginable painful words upon others. It was beyond out of control. Chloe got beat up twice within seven months and suffered further when videos of those fights showed up online and spread rapidly. We feared she would take her life or become addicted to drugs because of her growing self-hate.

If you have a teen that struggles with mental illness, these social media posts may sound all too familiar and may even make your stomach turn. During the teen years, kids are developing and understanding their identity and are often vulnerable to peer judgments and expectations. Compound that with the constant bombardment of posts from peers and a teen's budding identity can be compromised.

Anxiety is the most common mental-health disorder in the United States, affecting nearly one-third of both adolescents and adults, according to the National Institute of Mental Health. But unlike depression, with which it routinely occurs, anxiety is often seen as a less serious problem.

When asked about common sources of worry among highly anxious kids, teens don't hesitate: social media. Anxious teenagers from all backgrounds are relentlessly comparing themselves with their peers, she said, and the results are almost uniformly distressing.

Experts are hearing the same things over and over again among their teen clients and parents – kids aren't learning adequate interpersonal skills and resiliency due to using the screen as a shield to avoid tough situations and constant comparison.

Teen use of social media is at an all-time high and there are no signs of it slowing down. What mental health professionals around the globe are citing is that the use of social media during the last decade has contributed to increased teen depression, anxiety and related behaviors, including cutting, eating disorders and drug abuse.

Anxious kids certainly existed before Instagram, but many of the parents worry that their kids' digital habits — round-the-clock responding to texts, posting to social media, obsessively following the filtered exploits of peers — were partly to blame for their children's struggles. And anxious teens tend to agree.

A New York Times expose about teen mental health and social media outlined many of the issues teen's face and their perception. The Times reported that a college student went on a philosophical rant about his generation's relationship to social media. "I don't think we realize how much it's affecting our moods and personalities," he said. "Social media is a tool, but it's become this thing that we can't live without but that's making us crazy."[16]

In his case, he had little doubt that social media made him more self-conscious, reported the Times. "In high school, I'd constantly be judging my self-worth online," recalling his tortured relationship with social media. "I would think, 'Oh, people don't want to see me on their timeline.'"

While smartphones can provoke anxiety, they can also serve as a handy avoidance strategy. At the height of his struggles, one teen spent hours at a time on his phone at home or at school. "It was a way for me not to think about classes and college, not to have to talk to people," he said.

The Northwest Anxiety Institute in Portland, OR, clinical director Kevin Ashworth, warned in a parent training of the "illusion of control and certainty" that smartphones offer anxious young people desperate to manage their environments. "Teens will go places if they feel like they know everything that will happen, if they know everyone who will be there, if they can see who's checked in online," Ashworth told the parents. "But life doesn't always come with that kind of certainty, and they're never practicing the skill of rolling with the punches, of walking into an unknown or awkward social situation and learning that they can survive it."

Jean Twenge, a professor of psychology at San Diego State University who researches adolescent mental health and psychological differences among generations, used to be skeptical of those who sounded an alarm about teenage internet use. "It seemed like too easy an explanation for negative mental-health outcomes in teens, and there wasn't much evidence for it." She searched for other possible explanations, including economic ones. But the timing of the spike in anxious and depressed teenagers since 2011, which she called one of the sharpest and most significant she has seen, is "all wrong," she said. "The economy was improving by the time the increase started."

The more she looked for explanations, the more she kept returning to two seemingly unrelated trend lines — depression in teenagers and smartphone adoption. (There is significantly more data about depression than anxiety.) Since 2011, the trend lines increased at essentially the same rate. In her recent book "iGen," and in an article in The Atlantic, Twenge highlights a number of studies exploring the connection between social media and unhappiness. "The use of social media and smartphones look culpable for the increase in teen mental-health issues," she told me. "It's enough for an arrest — and as we get more data, it might be enough for a conviction."

Among many teachers and administrators, one word — "resiliency" — keeps coming up. More and more students struggle to recover from minor setbacks and aren't "equipped to problem-solve or advocate for themselves effectively." In the last few years, educators have watched in astonishment as more students struggle with anxiety — and as more of those "stop coming to school, because they just can't."

Social Media Use

Many parents worry about how exposure to technology might affect toddlers developmentally. We know our preschoolers are picking up new social and cognitive skills at a stunning pace, and we don't want hours spent glued to an iPad to impede that. But adolescence is an equally important period of rapid development, and too few of us are paying attention to how our teenagers' use of technology—much more intense and intimate than a 3-year-old playing with dad's iPhone—is affecting them. In fact, experts worry that the social media and text messages that have become so integral to teenage life are promoting anxiety and lowering self-esteem.

Indirect Communication

Teens are masters at keeping themselves occupied in the hours after school until way past bedtime. When they're not doing their homework (and when they are) they're online and on their phones, texting, sharing, trolling, scrolling, you name it. Of course before everyone had an Instagram account teens kept themselves busy, too, but they were more likely to do their chatting on the phone, or in person when hanging out at the mall. It may have looked like a lot of aimless hanging around, but what they were doing was experimenting, trying out skills, and succeeding and failing in tons of tiny real-time interactions that kids today are missing out on. For one thing, modern teens are learning to do most of their communication while looking at a screen, not another person.

There's no question kids are missing out on very critical social skills. "As a species we are very highly attuned to reading social cues," says Dr. Catherine Steiner-Adair, a clinical psychologist and author of The Big Disconnect. "There's no question kids are missing out on very critical social skills. In a way, texting and online communicating—it's not like it creates a nonverbal learning disability, but it puts everybody in a nonverbal disabled context, where body language, facial expression, and even the smallest kinds of vocal reactions are rendered invisible."

Lowering the Risks

Certainly speaking indirectly creates a barrier to clear communication, but that's not all. Learning how to make friends is a major part of growing up, and friendship requires a certain amount of risk-taking. This is true for making a new friend, but it's also true for maintaining friendships. When there are problems that need to be faced—big ones or small ones—it takes courage to be honest about your feelings and then hear what the other person has to say. Learning to effectively cross these bridges is part of what makes friendship fun and exciting, and also scary. "Part of healthy self-esteem is knowing how to say what you think and feel even when you're in disagreement with other people or it feels emotionally risky," notes Dr. Steiner-Adair.

But when friendship is conducted online and through texts, kids are doing this in a context stripped of many of the most personal—and sometimes intimidating—aspects of communication. It's easier to keep your guard up when you're texting, so less is at stake. You aren't hearing or seeing the effect that your words are having on the other person. Because the conversation isn't happening in real time, each party can take more time to consider a response. No wonder kids say calling someone on the phone is "too intense"—it requires more direct communication, and if you aren't used to that it may well feel scary.

If kids aren't getting enough practice relating to people and getting their needs met in person and in real time, many of them will grow up to be adults who are anxious about our species' primary means of communication—talking. And of course social negotiations only get riskier as people get older and begin navigating romantic relationships and employment.

Cyberbullying

The other big danger that comes from kids communicating more indirectly is that it has gotten easier to be cruel. "Kids text all sorts of things that you would never in a million years contemplate saying to anyone's face," says Dr. Donna Wick, a clinical and developmental psychologist who runs Mind to Mind Parent. She notes that this seems to be especially true of girls, who typically don't like to disagree with each other in "real life."

"You hope to teach them that they can disagree without jeopardizing the relationship, but what social media is teaching them to do is disagree in ways that are more extreme and do jeopardize the relationship. It's exactly what you don't want to have happen," she says.

Dr. Steiner-Adair agrees that girls are particularly at risk. "Girls are socialized more to compare themselves to other people, girls in particular, to develop their identities, so it makes them more vulnerable to the downside of all this." She warns that a lack of solid self-esteem is often to blame. "We forget that relational aggression comes from insecurity and feeling awful about yourself, and wanting to put other people down so you feel better."

Peer acceptance is a big thing for adolescents, and many of them care about their image as much as a politician running for office, and to them it can feel as serious. Add to that the fact that kids today are getting actual polling data on how much people like them or their appearance via things like "likes," and it's enough to turn anyone's head. Who wouldn't want to make herself look cooler if she can? So kids can spend hours pruning their online identities, trying to project an idealized image. Teenage girls sort through hundreds of photos, agonizing over which ones to post online. Boys compete for attention by trying to out-gross one other, pushing the envelope as much as they can in the already disinhibited atmosphere online. Kids gang up on each other and a mob mentality can take over.

Adolescents have always been doing this, but with the advent of social media they are faced with more opportunities—and more traps—than ever before. When kids scroll through their feeds and see how great everyone seems, it only adds to the pressure. We're used to worrying about the impractical ideals that photoshopped magazine models give to our kids, but what happens with the kid next door is photoshopped, too? Even more confusing, what about when your own profile doesn't really represent the person that you feel like you are on the inside?

"Adolescence and the early twenties in particular are the years in which you are acutely aware of the contrasts between who you appear to be and who you think you are," says Dr. Wick. "It's similar to the 'imposter syndrome' in psychology. As you get older and acquire more mastery, you begin to realize that you actually are good at some things, and then you feel that gap hopefully narrow. But imagine having your deepest darkest fear be that you aren't as good as you look, and then imagine needing to look that good all the time! It's exhausting."

As Dr. Steiner-Adair explains, "Self-esteem comes from consolidating who you are." The more identities you have, and the more time you spend pretending to be someone you aren't, the harder it's going to be to feel good about yourself.

Stalking (and Being Ignored)

Another big change that has come with new technology and especially smartphones is that we are never really alone. Kids update their status, share what they're watching, listening to, and reading, and have apps that let their friends know their specific location on a map at all times. Even if a person isn't trying to keep his friends updated, he's still never out of reach of a text message. The result is that kids feel hyperconnected with each other. The conversation never needs to stop, and it feels like there's always something new happening.

"Whatever we think of the 'relationships' maintained and in some cases initiated on social media, kids never get a break from them," notes Dr. Wick. "And that, in and of itself, can produce anxiety. Everyone needs a respite from the demands of intimacy and connection; time alone to regroup, replenish and just chill out. When you don't have that, it's easy to become emotionally depleted, fertile ground for anxiety to breed."

It's also surprisingly easy to feel lonely in the middle of all that hyperconnection. For one thing, kids now know with depressing certainty when they're being ignored. We all have phones and we all respond to things pretty quickly, so when you're waiting for a response that doesn't come, the silence can be deafening. The silent treatment might be a strategic insult or just the unfortunate side effect of an online adolescent relationship that starts out intensely but then fades away.

"In the old days when a boy was going to break up with you, he had to have a conversation with you. Or at least he had to call," says Dr. Wick. "These days he might just disappear from your screen, and you never get to have the 'What did I do?' conversation." Kids are often left imagining the worst about themselves."

But even when the conversation doesn't end, being in a constant state of waiting can still provoke anxiety. We can feel ourselves being put on the back burner, we put others back there, and our very human need to communicate is effectively delegated there, too.

What Should Parents Do?

Both Dr. Wick and Dr. Steiner-Aidair agreed that the best thing parents can do to minimize the risks associated with technology is to curtail their own consumption first. It's up to parents to set a good example of what healthy computer usage looks like. Most of us check our phones or our email too much, out of either real interest or nervous habit. Kids should be used to seeing our faces, not our heads bent over a screen. Establish technology-free zones in the house and technology-free hours when no one uses the phone, including mom and dad. "Don't walk in the door after work in the middle of a conversation," Dr. Steiner-Adair advises. "Don't walk in the door after work, say 'hi' quickly, and then 'just check your email.' In the morning, get up a half hour earlier than your kids and check your email then. Give them your full attention until they're out the door. And neither of you should be using phones in the car to or from school because that's an important time to talk."

Not only does limiting the amount of time you spend plugged in to computers provide a healthy counterpoint to the tech-obsessed world, it also strengthens the parent-child bond and makes kids feel more secure. Kids need to know that you are available to help them with their problems, talk about their day, or give them a reality check.

"It is the mini-moments of disconnection, when parents are too focused on their own devices and screens, that dilute the parent-child relationship," Dr. Steiner-Adair warns. And when kids start turning to the Internet for help or to process whatever happened during the day, you might not like what happens. "Tech can give your children more information than you can, and it doesn't have your values," notes Dr. Steiner-Adair. "It won't be sensitive to your child's personality, and it won't answer his question in a developmentally appropriate way."

In addition, Dr. Wick advises delaying the age of first use as much as possible. "I use the same advice here that I use when talking about kids and alcohol—try to get as far as you can without anything at all." If your child is on Facebook, Dr. Wick says that you should be your child's friend and monitor her page. But she advises against going through text messages unless there is cause for concern. "If you have a reason to be worried then okay, but it better be a good reason. I see parents who are just plain old spying on their kids. Parents should begin by trusting their children. To not even give your kid the benefit of the doubt is incredibly damaging to the relationship. You have to feel like your parents think you're a good kid."

Offline, the gold standard advice for helping kids build healthy self-esteem is to get them involved in something that they're interested in. It could be sports or music or taking apart computers or volunteering—anything that sparks an interest and gives them confidence. When kids learn to feel good about what they can do instead of how they look and what they own, they're happier and better prepared for success in real life. That most of these activities also involve spending time interacting with peers face-to-face is just the icing on the cake.

One of my daily reminders and affirmations: Be patient, caring and supportive. Life can be painful.

Friends & Peer Pressure

During a time of immense changes and growth, peer pressure can be challenging for teens. For an adolescent struggling with a mental illness, looking to fit in and be accepted feels like a necessity.

I was fairly "social" during my teen years and I will admit I had a night or more where alcohol was consumed. When I entered my freshman year, I began to have issues with anxiety and depression, though I didn't know what it was at the time. While developing into young women, my friends and I all yearned to be accepted, popular and attractive to boys. Alcohol made me feel more confident and not as self-conscious about what I was saying or doing. I could hide behind the buzz and not "feel" the intense anxiety or depression that was always dominating my psyche. Now that I'm the parent of two teenagers, I am keenly aware of why I drank alcohol in high school: 1.) to fit in and 2.) to repress my anxiety and depression, if only for a while. What I didn't know is that alcohol is a depressant and not such a good choice if you're struggling with a budding mental illness. Chloe had her first experience with alcohol at age 14. I'm fairly certain she was feeling quite a bit of peer pressure by her friend and the friend's parents who supplied the alcohol (don't get me started). She called me to come pick her up that evening because she said her "stomach hurt." When she got in the car, I immediately smelled alcohol and knew she was drunk. It took a little prodding for her to finally admit it. I got her home safely and tucked her into bed.

Jeff and I try to keep communication open with our girls and work to not overreact, since we have our own high school memories. The next day, I talked with Chloe about the dangers of mixing alcohol and drugs with the medication she takes for her mental illness. I shared with her that one of her anti-anxiety medications lowers her heart rate and alcohol can cause seizures and even death.

We also discussed the safety of her friend's house and how it is illegal to serve alcohol to minors. She is not allowed to stay at that friend's house again and is limited to where she can spend time with her.

Chloe is especially vulnerable to peer pressure. With her non-verbal learning disorder, she has a hard time reading body language, can't "read between the lines" and struggles to fit in with her peers. Not a good combination when a friend is pressuring her to drink. I hope since we responded calmly and honestly about the experience, she heard us. She did tell me and Jeff that she told her friend she wouldn't be drinking when she turns 21 since she could have a seizure.

Chapter 10—The Justice System

GETTING REAL: DARREN

Amy called it "the storm" — an uncontrollable outburst of rage that seized her first-born son, Darren, sending him into a Titanic meltdown of mad shrieks, punching fists and kicking feet.

These "storms" started when he was around two, prime time for independent toddlers to test boundaries, but she soon realized that Darren's outbursts weren't like the typical tantrums her friends' children pitched.

She also recognized characteristics of obsessive-compulsive disorder, which she, her father and sister all had been treated for. Darren would carefully line up his toy cars, then collapse in howls of hurt and anger if someone moved one. He obsessed over keeping track of the hat his figure of Woody from "Toy Story" wore, bringing family life to a screeching halt if he couldn't find the tiny cowboy hat.

As Darren grew, so did the storms. When he didn't get his way he would tear apart his room in completely unregulated episodes that left him with a headache, sweaty and exhausted but remorseful. Amy said it was almost like he left his body or was possessed. Darren's stepfather, who Amy married when her son was 2, sometimes would wrap his arms around the boy to keep him from harm.

The family always had to have a back-up plan for leaving a fun event like a bowling outing in case Darren had a meltdown. They let him win board games to avoid an ordeal. His sister, four years younger, would run to her room and hide when something set Darren off.

One day when Darren was 9, Amy was finishing up a phone call before taking the kids out to play. Impatient, Darren grabbed a knife and leapt onto Amy's back, demanding she go outside. Her world in a whirl, she called a mental health hotline that recommended she take him to the hospital.

The on-shift psychiatrist had no pediatric experience, but admitted Darren. Five days in the hospital seemed to reset the chaos in his brain. The hospitalization also connected the family to a pediatric psychiatrist who instantly suspected Darren was bipolar and put him on a mood stabilizer and an antidepressant that seemed to work, at least for a while.

His OCD caused him to obsess over things until he seemed to be in physical pain. When some new possession or desire gripped his brain, he keened about his wants, making wild promises and doing and saying anything to try to get that new video game or whatever he wanted. A neuropsychologist who treated him said Darren exhibited some of the most severe obsessive thoughts he had seen.

School was a struggle. Darren would run away from class or be so immobilized by anxiety that he would just put his head down and fall asleep. He was put on an Individualized Education Program and finished sixth grade, but things fell apart when he moved on to middle school.

He couldn't handle the noise and crowds of seventh grade. He would act out defiantly in class and be sent to the office. Once when he was sent to the office, he was so desperate to call his mom and explain what was happening that he pushed the school secretary.

The strict disciple of one classroom program didn't work, but neither did the collaborative problem-solving approach used during a six-month residential stay, where Darren lied and manipulated staff to get his way. He was then sent to a secure facility in a nearby town but escaped.

Back in a day school program, Darren used information disclosed in group therapy to pick at and provoke other kids. He wouldn't take responsibility for the ensuing fight, instead saying he had been targeted. After throwing rocks at other students, he fled and was picked up by police.

As his history of violence and escapes grew, the family struggled to find programs that could provide the services he needed. Finally, they turned to the county mental health department. Cognitive behavioral therapy at home showed promise, but then he stopped cooperating with the therapist and skills trainer sent to work with him.

The big storm finally hit when Darren was 14. He punched Amy in the stomach in front of his care team at the county health department. They called police and put him in a secure holding area where he quickly calmed down. Everyone agreed he needed residential treatment, but to get it, he would have to be evaluated at the hospital and get a referral while he was in crisis.

Amy was fearful every day about what Darren might do, but she knew he needed help so she found herself provoking him, hoping to cause the storm that would push him into a safe harbor. When he finally came unhinged, she called police and the same officer who had responded when he punched her at the county mental health offices came to the house. Darren was taken to the hospital in handcuffs. He had just turned 14.

Inevitably, and possibly frequently, there will be times that violent and disruptive behavior takes place. Unfortunately, due to the rapid cycling of children with mental illness, managing the rages or storms may be daily or multiple times during the day.

It will be a process to find the best set of solutions for your child but, to start, try these tips below to help manage and mitigate unacceptable behavior:

- When you and your youth are BOTH calm, explain to him/her what kinds of behaviors you will not tolerate, as well as the specific consequences upon which you (and other family members) have decided (and agreed) for specific violent and disruptive behaviors. Example: "Next time you threaten to harm any of us, the police will be called."

- Get to know and recognize cues that your child is becoming violent or disruptive. (Your own uneasiness or fear is usually a good cue. Dogs also serve as a great cue. Our Australian Shepherd used to whine when Chloe started to get wound up.)

- Tell your youth that his/her behavior is scaring you or upsetting you. This feedback can defuse the situation, but proceed with the next suggestion if it does not. Saying you are scared does NOT mean you act scared. With this said, it is IMPERATIVE that you maintain control and demonstrate you are calling the shots.

- If you (and other family members) have made a limit-setting plan, now is the time to carry out the consequences. If you have not already warned your child of the consequences when he/she was calm, use your judgment and past experience to decide whether to warn him/her or to just go ahead with the plan without saying anything.

- Give your child plenty of space, both physical and emotional. Never corner a person who is agitated unless you have the ability to restrain him/her. Verbal threats or hostile remarks from you constitute emotional cornering and should be avoided.

- Give yourself an easy exit, and leave the scene IMMEDIATELY if he/she is scaring you or becoming violent.

- Get help! Just bringing in other people, particularly the police, can quickly defuse the situation.

- If your youth is over 18 and someone else has witnessed him/her committing a violent or dangerous act, whoever witnessed that act can petition for involuntary commitment.

What Shouldn't You Do During A Rage/Storm?

- Do NOT try to ignore violent or disruptive behavior. Ignoring only leads your youth to believe that this kind of behavior is acceptable and "repeatable."

- Do NOT give your child what he/she wants if the way he/she is trying to get it through bullying you. Giving in reinforces this bullying behavior and makes it likely that he/she will use it again. Only give in of it is the ONLY way out of a dangerous situation.

- Do NOT try to lecture or reason with your youth when he/she is agitated or losing control.
- NEVER be alone with someone you fear. For instance, do not drive him or her to the hospital by yourself.

If You Have to Call the Police

According to the National Alliance on Mental Illness, people experiencing a mental illness crisis are more likely to encounter the police that to get medical help. And the number one topic to their help line is calls from families trying to find help for a mentally ill family member that has been arrested.

Unfortunately, the prospects for a mentally ill person that gets into the judicial system are not always promising. But as a parent trying to provide the best possible care for your child, there may still be times when calling the police is the best solution to the crisis moment.

"We called the police on both of our children," a friend Sandy shared recently, "only when we felt threatened. For our son, we felt our lives were threatened. And for our daughter, we felt her life was threatened; we called and asked for a welfare check for her. I think those would be the only two situations to call in law enforcement. "

Over half of the states in the US require police personnel to be trained in responding to mental health or behavioral issues, and several states also have crisis intervention teams in place. Their mandate is to connect those in a mental health crisis to social and medical services rather than processing them through the justice system.

The criteria they use will generally follow these guidelines:

- Risk or threat assessment – Is your child at risk of harming themselves or others? Is the threat temporary (occurring in a single situation of frustration or overstimulation) or an ongoing occurrence? Do they have access to items they may need to carry out their threat? Is their behavior consistent with what they've communicated?

Note that if the incident happens at school, each school district will also have its assessment guidelines that may take place before the police are involved. Contact your local school district for their specific guidelines or to find out when parent notification is supposed to take place in their notification process. The school should have a record of your child's diagnosed mental illness (that you have provided) and any education plan related to their illness on file.

- Removal and/or referral – If the threat is considered ongoing or a crisis situation (someone is under threat of serious harm), the choice may be to remove your child to a hospital or to police custody. If a hospital is the next step, they will be physically and psychologically assessed, and recommendations made based on that assessment. If they are taken into police custody, the police department will assess the need for referral to a support option (i.e. a mental health counselor or social service resource) or for pressing charges and detaining them through the legal system.

If your child is taken to jail, there may be a limited number of steps you can take, depending on the age of your child.

- Inform the police officer, detective and the jail's booking department of your child's mental health diagnosis, including any medications they are taking and their medication schedule.
- Contact your medical team to inform them of the arrest.
- Request any local advocacy programs they can recommend.
- Recognize that a family awareness or social service child advocacy program may be brought in on your child's case.
- If they don't know any local connections, contact NAMI or NIMH for local resources they can recommend, or any online or phone support they can offer.
- Contact legal representation as required.

While it is encouraging to see intervention being acknowledged as the best possible way to deflect the mentally ill from the criminal justice system, unfortunately, not every system operates as smoothly as planned or intended. Depending on the circumstances of the moment, or the resources available in each district, your child may end up in jail instead of in a hospital or treatment center.

Sadly, this turned out to be Sandy's experience. "We have now had two adult children with mental health issues go through the criminal justice system (and I say "we" because I could not have done this without my husband). ... When our son was a teenager, his mental health therapist kept saying the only way we would be able to get help for him was to get into the criminal justice system. I can't remember exactly why though, and when I asked my husband he said he remembers that being said too and he now says 'and that's bullshit.'"

"Our daughter's experience is more recent and we developed a relationship with a local police officer who was called on her numerous times. She was bothering people and he could see she was mentally ill and in need of help. He told us he would monitor closely and arrest her as soon as he had cause as he assumed that she would get a mental health evaluation when arrested. Unfortunately, she was released from jail and back out on the streets within hours with a criminal arrest record for life and no mental health evaluation. During that whole two hours I was on a crisis mental health line trying to get her help, to no avail."

"I could tell that the officer dealing with our daughter seemed to care and have her best interests at heart. For that I am truly grateful even though the rest of our experience with the criminal justice system left a bad taste. In hindsight, we wish that it all could have been prevented but I'm not sure how when it boils down to a life-threatening situation in the moment."

"When our [adult] son was taken to the jail, we were not able to visit him as there was a no contact order put in place. So we were not able to support our very ill son. We called the jail and asked if he could be given his medication and put on a suicide watch but were not told if this would be done," recalls Sandy.

The National Association of Mental Illness has published a guide for families trying to navigate the legal system (listed in the resources section of this book) but it's also important to remember that each state will have differing legislations around this matter of mentally ill defendants in the court system.

"Our experience with the court system is that they give no heed to a person having a mental health condition. Our son was advised by his

187

public defender to plead guilty. In hindsight, he would have been much better off pleading no contest," Sandy has since learned. "A criminal arrest record does not help a mentally ill person get work."

Her summation based on her experience: "The criminal justice system did not serve us well and we would recommend avoiding it at all costs, except for life-threatening situations of course. "

You may find the legal system as confusing or as difficult to navigate as the healthcare system, but remember, you are still your child's best advocate.

National Association of Mental Illness Helpline:
800-950-NAMI or text "NAMI" to 741741

Chapter 11—Relapse and Recovery

GETTING REAL: BRANDON

Sitting in a family counseling session at an Oregon substance abuse treatment center, Pat thought her 15-year-old son was making a "Sixth Sense" joke when he said something about seeing dead people.

Long before getting in trouble – first for drinking during the school day as a freshman, then for having a marijuana pipe on school grounds at the start of his sophomore year–Brandon had been a quirky class clown and a wildly imaginative storyteller.

But this time, he wasn't kidding.

With coaxing from his therapist, he explained to his mom, Pat, an elementary school teacher, and dad, John, a construction manager, that he saw things that didn't exist, things he knew weren't real.

His care team at the in-patient treatment center couldn't be sure what was causing the hallucinations. They could be a side effect of the Prozac he had started taking because seeking treatment in such a center could cause anxiety and Brandon had never been good at transitions. They could be caused by his lack of sleep or the melatonin he took to help that. Or they could be a separate mental illness.

One thing soon became clear; the rehab center wasn't the place for Brandon. His hallucinations worsened. The voices told him he wasn't safe there. He tried to run away multiple times.

Pat and John brought Brandon home. The auditory hallucinations continued with voices telling Brandon to kill himself.

Nights were the worse. Brandon would stay up all night pacing. Sometimes Pat would drive around with him through the darkness. He would say he was a danger to himself and others and needed immediate medical help so, at his request, his parents would take him to the emergency room, get medication and bring him home again.

The family connected with a psychiatrist who was part of an Early Assessment and Support Team, which works to reduce long-term disability associated with psychosis by providing clinical and community support to young people experiencing psychosis. But before Brandon could settle into the program, his condition worsened. He was self-medicating with marijuana, which had at first made his hallucinations go away, but when they returned, they were more graphic than before.

With Brandon's drug use and penchant for running away and staying out with friends, his parents just wanted a secure place for him. They had secure transport pick him up and take him to a secure home farm for children.

The care team there worked to get him on the right medication to quiet the voices and stem his anxiety. By April of the next year, the family's insurance company had concluded he was no longer a danger to himself and should return home for continuing care.

This pattern would become frustratingly familiar. In treatment Brandon made positive progress and insurers would declare him well, but outside that controlled environment, he spiraled into trouble. Pat described it as getting a Band-aid when he needs a future.

Hoping to avoid being tempted back into substance abuse, Brandon went to live with Pat's parents in another state instead of returning to his hometown, where he knew where and how to find drugs easily. He had spent the summer after his freshman year of high school with his grandparents, too, hoping to break away from the drinking that had first landed him in trouble.

The family struggled to find a care provider in that state to deal with Brandon's combination of addiction and generalized anxiety disorder and a schizophrenic-like condition that experts didn't want to diagnose as schizophrenia because his substance abuse issues could cause similar symptoms. Insurance would only cover treatment that dealt with both Brandon's substance abuse and other mental health issues, but most providers only dealt with one or the other. The family finally turned to a county health department, but the therapist there said Brandon was a thug, just using the supposed voices in his head as an excuse for bad behavior.

Recognizing the situation there was untenable, he returned home.

Back in state, his condition failed to improve and he was soon living on the streets, using whatever drugs he could get for free. He hung out at a convenience store, charging his phone there so he could stay in touch with his mom. He finally called her, asking for help dealing with his illness.

Everything is smooth sailing and suddenly your child is acting out or in a funk and declining quickly. You immediately see the signs of them slipping back into a relapse...

Relapses are a bitter reminder that a mental illness must always be managed. I received a message from a college friend recently that her 14-year-old Asperger's daughter had been admitted to inpatient treatment for severe depression. Her daughter is a cutter and had a similar episode a year ago. People cut to mask the pain they feel inside; to distract them from it. For many, it's a very shameful behavior but one that can become addictive quickly. Other behaviors that mask internal pain are drinking too much, overworking, gambling, shopping (guilty), eating disorders, the list goes on. Chloe struggles with depression too and for a kid with Asperger's, it can often go unnoticed because of their deep thinking, and often, introverted personality. My friend's message perked up my awareness and reminded me of the importance of checking in with both my girls. It's easy to get wrapped up in my own thoughts and life and forget to be conscious of my daughters' behaviors and body language, especially Chloe's. Sophia is good at expressing her feelings but Chloe struggles with identifying what her feelings are in the present. It can take weeks for her to process them then connect feelings to thoughts and words. I want to thank my friend for sharing with me her family's current struggles with her daughter. It was a good reminder for me to be aware of our loved ones, especially those who struggle, and check in periodically.

RELAPSE AND RECOVERY

Whether consciously or not, the question seems to always be lurking in the back of our mind: When will it happen again? When will my child come unglued, lose it, fly out of control? Unfortunately, there is no pat answer and it can vary greatly from child to child. If your child does relapse, you need to have a plan of action and some tools to manage the situation.

Early Warning Signs Before a Relapse

Keeping in tune with your child's mental health is critical to managing their illness and trying to keep the peace in your house. In my friend Alison's case she started to see her son's agitation and violence increase over time. The final straw was when he punched her in the stomach twice while at the psychiatrist's office. She knew it was time to intervene with more serious treatment.

The following are some warning signs to pay attention to and seek professional help if you believe your child is relapsing.

Primary Warning Signs:

- Feeling more tense or nervous.
- Having more trouble sleeping.
- Change in activity level.
- Having more trouble concentrating.

- Feeling paranoid or that people are talking about them.

Other Warning Signs:

Feeling more depressed	Hearing voices or seeing things
Losing interest in things they like doing	Feeling someone else is controlling them
Seeing friends less	Decreased hygiene
Enjoying things less	Easily angered
Eating less or more	More bad dreams or nightmares
Preoccupied with one or two ideas	Thoughts of hurting themselves or others
Having trouble making sense when talking	More aggressive or pushy
Forgetting things more	Too excited or overactive
Feeling worthless	Trouble relating to others
Feeling crazy	Frequent aches and pains
Feeling badly for no reason	Higher alcohol or drug use

If a relapse does occur, seek professional psychiatric services immediately. It is important to remain calm and be patient and gentle with your child, yourself and other family members. It's difficult to manage a fragile mind during crisis but it is nobody's fault and anger and blame only serve to feed into the mental illness and dysfunctional family behaviors.

If you fear the relapse is psychotic, there are some critical guidelines to follow to avoid aggressive or dangerous behavior:

- Don't threaten.
- Don't shout.
- Don't criticize.
- Don't argue with other family members.
- Don't bait the youth.
- Don't stand over the youth; if he/she is seated, sit down as well.
- Avoid direct, continuous eye contact or touching.
- Don't block a doorway unless it is an exit.

What to Expect During Recovery

After your youth has been treated, it's easy to assume that they'll be "back to normal" and able to perform routine daily activities. Typically, this isn't the case. Healthy parents and siblings often have a hard time accepting that it may take some time for the ill child to perform at a level previous to their relapse. Just like someone who has had major surgery, recovery is necessary to adequately heal and repair.

Family Tips During Recovery:

- **Go slow.** Recovery takes time. Rest is important. Things will get better in their own time.
- **Keep it cool.** Enthusiasm is normal; tone it down. Disagreement is normal; tone it down too.
- **Give them space.** Time out is important. It's okay to offer. It's okay to refuse.
- **Set limits.** Everyone needs to know what the rules are. A few good rules keep things calmer.
- **Ignore what you can't change.** Let some things slide. Don't ignore violence.
- **Keep it simple.** Say what you have to say clearly, calmly, positively.
- **Follow doctor's orders.** Take medications as they are prescribed. Take only medications that are prescribed.
- **Carry on business as usual.** Re-establish family routines as quickly as possible. Stay in touch with family members.
- No street drugs or alcohol. They make symptoms worse.

- **Pick up on early signs.** Note changes. Consult with your physician.
- **Solve problems step by step.** Make changes gradually. Work on one thing at a time.
- **Lower expectations, temporarily.** Use a personal yardstick. Compare this month to last month rather than last year or next year.
- **Keep it cool at home.** If work gets hectic, remember to keep a low-key environment at home.
- **Punctuality and attendance are crucial.** Everyone in the family needs to help out.
- **Work is hard.** Developing work skills is difficult. Social skills can wait.

Chapter 12—Caring for Yourself and Your Family

GETTING REAL: JOHN

When Linda and her husband adopted their son, John, they knew there was a possibility he had mental health issues. They adopted John when he was an infant. His birth parents were young, about 15 years old, and came from rough families themselves. John's birth mother had been diagnosed as bipolar, and was on medication for her mental health issues.

In addition to being with her son, Linda also works nights as a hospital monitor tech. She and her husband saw signs of potential mental health issues in John from a young age. Now six years old, John has been diagnosed with autism spectrum disorder and bipolar disorder.

When John was about one year old, Linda says it was a struggle to get him dressed. John also didn't interact with his parents in the same way other children interacted with their families. He seemed apathetic toward his parents. When he was two years old, the daycare facility noticed John had problems transitioning from one activity to the next; he would pull himself out of the group of kids, self-soothe himself, and he struggled playing with the other children and not wanting to interact with them. From there, the situation spiraled downward.

John was more aggressive, and he would become embroiled in tantrums which lasted a couple of hours. At daycare, he demolished everything. He threw chairs, broke a table, and would bite and hit the other kids. He became physically volatile. That was the first real time Linda and her husband believed something was wrong.

John would do the same things at home as in daycare. He'd go into rages that would last 2-3 hours where he would throw things and bite or hit people. They had to lock up their animals because John was physically abusive to them. Linda watched her son and it was like seeing a switch flipped inside of him; suddenly he was a completely different child.

They were referred to an early intervention center, where John was evaluated by the staff. The center determined there were issues with John's motor skills, but did nothing to address his aggression. Linda and her husband were frustrated with the whole experience. The doctors rushed them in, spent only 30-60 minutes with John, rushed out, and then made a quick diagnosis. Doctors merely ran through a checklist and didn't get to know John or learn about his specific situation.

The early intervention center was one of many negative experiences for Linda and her family. A therapist told them John was possessed, and she and her husband were accused of being bad parents. They were also referred to the Child Development and Rehabilitation Center at OHSU, but John's behavior only continued to escalate.

Linda and her husband felt hopeless. No one believed them, and they tried everything they were told to do. The confinement of a timeout only triggered a fight response in John. He would kick and bite, and try to escape. John's rages continued, and at times he would bite Linda's legs and stomach. They couldn't raise their voices or get angry because John fed off of their emotions. If Linda cried, John would get angrier or fall apart and sob for hours. It was a living nightmare.

A friend recommended them to a psychiatric nurse practitioner. She listened, watched, and interacted with John. This started them down the road of realizing John was autistic and had a mood disorder. He was having autistic meltdowns where he could not communicate because of sensory overload, and mood swings with no cues or indications.

For Linda, every day was a roller coaster. John believed there were monsters trying to kill her, and then sometimes said he was the monster who would kill her. He described gory, violent things at three years old, and had night terrors they couldn't wake him from. John would see spiders and other things that weren't there, and would throw up because he was so terrified.

The roller coaster continued. John would be in a good place one day, and then spiral down again. They eventually started him on medication, but the types and amount of medication continued to change. His autism and mood disorder clashed with each other. A change in his routine would cause extreme mood swings, and he couldn't re-regulate himself. John would kick or bite, and then be angry with himself afterward. John would say he didn't want to be alive anymore. It agonized Linda to see the torment in his eyes.

Finding time for yourself and other family members when your mentally ill child is constantly in crisis is challenging, if not impossible. But as many of us have learned through hard experience, it's equally important that you learn how to maintain your sanity and get time for peace.

Taking Care of the Caregiver

As parents, we work hard to keep our mentally ill youth calm and cared for, as well as our other family members and household. It is so important to try to find time to take care of yourself too. Whether it's creating a plan with your partner, enlisting family help or relying on a friend or neighbor, try to make time to get away a few hours a week and have some solace.

- Be gentle with yourself. You are doing the best you can and this is NOT your fault. The same is true of your spouse or partner.

- Remind yourself that you are a loving helper, not a magician. None of us can change anyone else—we can only change the way that we relate to others.
- Find a place where you can be a hermit – use it every day – or whenever you need to.
- Learn to give support, praise and encouragement to those around you – and learn to accept it in return.
- Remember that in light of all the pain we see around us, we are bound to feel helpless at times. We need to be able to admit this without shame. Just caring and in being there, we are doing something important.
- Learn to vary your routine often and to change your tasks whenever possible.
- Learn to know the difference between complaining that relieves tension and the complaining that reinforces it.
- On your way home from work or even errands, focus on one good thing that happened during the day.
- Become a resource to yourself! Be creative and open to new approaches to old things.
- Use the support you give to others or a "buddy" system regularly. Use these as a support, for reassurance and to redirect yourself.
- Avoid "shop talk" during your breaks or when socializing with colleagues.
- Learn to use the expression "I choose to..." rather than expressions like "I have to…, "I ought to…," or "I should…"
- Learn to say, "I won't..." rather than "I can't..."
- Learn to say "no" and mean it, particularly to outside commitments that will only drain your reserves. If you can't say "no" – what is your "yes" worth?
- Aloofness and indifference are far more harmful than admitting to an inability to do more.
- Above all else – learn to laugh and play.

How to Hold Your Family Together

When you have a child with mental illness, it is easy to let your concern for them grow to consume your life, and it certainly increases the pressure on every other relationship in your family circle. Here are some things to remember:

Take Care of Yourself

While it is your responsibility to care for and support your child, it is also your responsibility to take care of yourself.

You may have to adjust your priorities or your lifestyle.

Avoid letting the challenges posed by your child's mental health condition make you neglect other important parts of your life.

In some cases, the stress of raising a child with a mental illness can contribute to the experience of mental health challenges by a parent. If you begin to feel that you are struggling with sadness or anxiety, do not hesitate to seek treatment for yourself.

Caring for your own mental well-being will serve as a model for your child to follow, and ensure that you are healthy and able to care for your child.

Take Care of Your Family

If you are married or co-parenting, navigating the care of your mentally ill child can place significant pressure on your relationship with your significant other. Personality styles, parenting styles, disciplinary styles all serve as sources of support, or of conflict. If things are getting bumpy between you and your partner, reach out to each other and to outside help if you need it. Remember that you're on the same team.

Remember, too, that if you have other children, they may resent being pushed to the side if all the attention is placed on their sibling's mental health challenges. Make sure that they understand what their sibling is going through, and that you spend time with each of them. Keeping a happy and balanced family can be very helpful in reducing stress levels for everyone, which can help alleviate symptoms of mental illness.

Get Your Family Involved

If you live with a partner or spouse, or have other children, try to get them involved in being an advocate for your child. You may find that you deal with challenges and obstacles differently than them, but you should find ways to combine strengths to overcome any weaknesses. Be ready to compromise, listen and be open to new ideas.

It is possible you may discover that some members of your family have little interest in supporting you and your child in dealing with challenges posed by your child's mental health condition. It is also possible that a spouse or significant other may be a negative influence on your child. They may demand discipline for behaviors your child cannot control, deny that there is anything wrong or insist upon an irrational course of action. Helping to raise a child who has a mental health condition can be stressful, and it is unrealistic to assume that anyone, yourself included, will always react in an ideal way. However, you must also realize that it is your responsibility to protect your child, even from others that you care about.

See more at: https://www.nami.org/Find-Support/Family-Members-and-Caregivers/Learning-to-Help-Your-Child-and-Your-Family#sthash.Z63y9xmR.dpuf

Learn All that You Can

Sometimes, the sea of information can be overwhelming, contradictory, or can change on a seemingly daily basis. But the more you know, the better you can advocate for your child's health, education and treatment. Find trusted resources and build your support team. Know your child - you are the best expert on their moods, patterns and struggles!

And know yourself. Having a child with a mental illness will teach you things about yourself that you would never know otherwise, and help you as you negotiate each day or know the places you need to find additional help.

NAMI

Whenever a friend or acquaintance informs me that their family is suddenly dealing with mental illness, I recommend they contact their local chapter of the National Alliance on Mental Illness (NAMI). I recommend NAMI to you, too. This organization can help you get started on your journey of learning about your child's condition, treatment options, and how to live with someone who suffers from mental illness.

With nearly 1,000 affiliates across the country, NAMI offers many, many free services for patients and family members. Key among these are educational classes and support groups, which are led by volunteers who have lived through the same thing you are living through.

NAMI Basics is an educational program for parents and other family caregivers of children and adolescents who have either been diagnosed with a mental health condition or who are experiencing symptoms but have not yet been diagnosed. This course is also available in Spanish.

NAMI Family-to-Family class is for families, partners, and friends of individuals with mental illness. Designated as an evidence-based program by SAMHSA, this course is designed to facilitate a better understanding of mental illness, increase coping skills, and empower participants to become advocates for their family members. This course is also available in Spanish.

NAMI Family Support Groups are routine support groups for family members, partners and friends of individuals living with a mental illness.

NAMI Smarts for Advocacy is a hands-on advocacy training program that helps concerned people to transform their passion and lived experience into skillful grassroots advocacy.

To find information about local classes or groups, you can start at NAMI's programs page at https://www.nami.org/Find-Support/NAMI-Programs.

Recognize the Potholes

Every family has a routine that can become upset through situations not directly connected to mental illness. For example, let's talk about back to school season. Or the holidays.

The holidays can be stressful for anyone. For someone with a mental illness, they can be the trigger that launches a mental episode or derails healthy habits and routine.

I don't know why it takes us off guard, but it does. Every darn year, the pattern is the same…One crazy issue after another. It always starts in late October. The newness of school must be wearing off and with the holidays right around the corner, it's prime time for Chloe to get distracted and fall off track.

Then comes November. Out-of-town guests, parties, shopping, baking, cleaning and everything unpredictable from Thanksgiving to Christmas interrupts the routine mentally ill people need to stay healthy.

Routine and consistency are key for those of us who struggle with a mental illness. With the hustle and bustle of the holiday season, that routine goes right out the window and it seems all rationale does too! As I shared with a friend, whose son struggles with bipolar disorder, one year Chloe had the good judgment (insert sarcasm) of lying to a friend's dad to throw a party at our house while we were gone, sneaking out to meet a friend while grounded, and announcing to all her Facebook friends that her mom (that's me!) may put her on birth control because she's freaked out some jerk will take advantage of her.

Needless-to-say, life gets a little hectic and stressful around our house during these seasons. To compound the issues, Jeff and I don't always agree on how to handle the situations.

I'm typically more conversational in my approach and ask lots of questions, like, "What the he!! are you doing?" and "How come you're sneaking out? Your dad is going to kill you!" I internalize my stress which generally manifests into migraines, a tight neck, and near nervous breakdowns, none of which are particularly productive.

Jeff, on the other hand, can only bottle his emotions up for so long before he explodes, usually resulting in a shut down by everyone in the family including the dogs and cats, who hide under chairs, in corners and behind doors in spare bathrooms.

When stress is at its peak, it's hard to stop and regroup. But knowing these events will happen (the holidays always happen, right?) means that we can be somewhat proactive about minimizing the impact they have on our family's routine.

Try to prevent stress during the holidays, especially if they have taken an emotional toll on you in the past. As difficult as it can be, the best approach is often one of unconditional love and empathy. Be gentle on yourself and loved one and take steps to ease stress.

How to Make the Holidays Happier

- ▶ **Acknowledge your feelings.** Whether the holidays trigger anxiety, depression, mania or everything in between, owning your feelings is the first step to gaining control of your situation. It's OK to take time to express your feelings and be true to yourself.
- ▶ **Reach out.** If your mental illness symptoms are getting the best of you, seek out support or help from support groups, therapists or through community, religious or other social events. Volunteering your time to help others also is a good way to lift your spirits, distract you from trying symptoms and connect you with new people.
- ▶ **Be realistic.** The holidays don't have to be perfect or just like last year. As families change and grow, traditions and rituals often change as well. Choose a few to hold on to, and be open to creating new ones. For example, if your usual group can't get together this year, find new ways to celebrate, such as sharing pictures, emails or videos.
- ▶ **Set aside differences.** Try to accept family members and friends as they are, even if they don't live up to all of your expectations. Set aside grievances until a more appropriate time for discussion. And be understanding if others get upset or distressed when something goes awry. Chances are they're feeling the effects of holiday stress, too.
- ▶ **Stick to a budget.** Before you go gift and food shopping, decide how much money you can afford to spend. Then stick to your budget. Don't try to buy happiness with an avalanche of gifts.
- ▶ **Plan ahead.** Set aside specific days for shopping, baking, visiting friends and other activities. Plan your menus and then make your shopping list. That will help prevent last-minute scrambling to buy forgotten ingredients. And make sure to line up help for party prep and cleanup.
- ▶ **Learn to say no.** Saying yes when you should say no can leave you feeling resentful and overwhelmed. Friends and colleagues will understand if you can't participate in every project or activity. If it's not possible to say no when your boss asks you to work overtime, try to remove something else from your agenda to make up for the lost time.
- ▶ **Don't abandon healthy habits.** Don't let the holidays become a free-for-all. Overindulgence only adds to your stress and guilt. Get ...

How to Make the Holidays Happier (cont.)

plenty of sleep, exercise and try to make healthy food choices in between festivities.

▶ **Take a breather.** Make some time for yourself. Spending just 15 minutes alone, without distractions, may refresh you enough to handle everything you need to do. Find something that reduces stress by clearing your mind, slowing your breathing and restoring inner calm... listen to music, take a bath and reading are all relaxing options.

▶ **Seek professional help if you need it.** Despite your best efforts, you may find yourself feeling persistently sad, anxious, manic, plagued by physical complaints, unable to sleep, irritable and hopeless, and unable to face routine chores. If these feelings last for a while, talk to your doctor or a mental health professional.

Chapter 13—Change Must Come

Tragic endings due to mental illness are all too familiar these days. If you haven't witnessed similar incidents yourself—maybe even with a member of your own family—you've almost certainly seen such scenes on the news. It happens all the time. And for days and weeks after heinous crimes occur at the hands of mentally ill persons, we see a huge uproar in Congress and in the media about gun control. But where's the uproar for legislation and resources to address mental illness?

Research shows that 300,000 incarcerated people are mentally ill in America's prisons, while only 30,000 are in mental health facilities seeking treatment. Our system is broken on all levels—public schools, health care, and the justice system. It's time for action and change and it starts with education, parent and family support and a shift in attitudes and perceptions in our schools, health care facilities and insurance and justice system.

While writing this book, I spoke with a mother who had to hire an attorney to sue her child's school district because it would not provide her mentally ill daughter with legally required support. My husband and I had to do the same thing years ago. Our families fought against different school districts that engaged in the same tactics of hiding information and lying about legally mandated services. Although both of our families had the financial resources to take legal action, it was a miserable time for us. And, worse, many other families faced with the same challenges can't afford attorneys or the time and emotional energy it takes to deal with dysfunctional systems and a problematic, mentally ill child. Then people wonder why such kids drop out of school, get in trouble, do drugs, or take a gun onto a campus full of students.

We must change how we—and the system—care for our mentally ill citizens. As it is, the system is not proactive, but reactive. When a man rants with a gun in a neighborhood full of families and young children and he isn't arrested or hospitalized because he didn't hurt anyone, the system is dangerously broken, not just in the justice system but also in health care, our schools, our insurance provisions, and across our culture.

Resources, the status quo, and the mental health system are not working and seem to be getting progressively worse.

What can we do?

We need to share the realities of mental illness:

- Mental illness is a brain disease and people cannot control it. Just like diabetes or any other life-threatening illnesses, mental illness often needs to be treated with medication and therapy.
- Mental illness impacts all walks of life – tall, short; men, women; wealthy, poor; Americans, Canadians, French, Asian, Russian…
- Treating mental illness is not a one-size-fits-all situation. Concurrent disabilities, opposing symptoms, and overloaded medical professionals make accurate diagnoses challenging, and effective treatment fluid. Difficult transitions often trigger or worsen symptoms of a mentally ill person. And they are often unable to evaluate their own condition.
- Partners and caregivers of mentally ill people need to have patience and compassion. It's not easy for them and like any other life-threatening disease, there are unexpected complications and it is often an unpredictable life.

Above all, we need to talk more about mental illness. We need to share the facts—the reality—in order to minimize the stigma and shame associated with the disorders and diseases that cause people to become mentally ill. We need people to know that they're not alone and that helpful information and resources are available. We need to connect, to learn from each other, and to create solutions. And we need to learn, to gain knowledge so that we can navigate the maze of challenges—and overcome them.

Looking Forward, With Hope

Through my years of experience with Chloe and with other families who are struggling with mentally ill children, I've come to believe that the single most important factor in managing mental illness is early intervention and advocacy. But this is only possible when several key factors are aligned: awareness, acceptance, adequate resources, proper treatment, and an understanding and compassionate school environment.

As someone with a mental illness and a mother of a mentally ill child, what I'm certain of is while the disease can be managed, it is often a lifelong condition that needs continuous awareness and vigilant self-care. We take life day-by-day and continue to accept Chloe, our family and the situation for what it is.

Awareness and Acceptance. I have personal experience with my own mental illness, so I recognized early on that Chloe struggled with many of the same issues I do. But denial runs deep, and acceptance in the family and among friends didn't always come easily. It has taken years to educate others about the facts of youth mental illness, such as the fact that symptoms can emerge as early as two years of age. The process of learning and accepting is ongoing.

Resources. We are fortunate to have had the family resources to support our decisions. Diagnosis and treatment are expensive. It costs money to see psychiatrists, seek treatment, try endless alternative therapy modes, and engage attorneys to secure the federally mandated services to which your child is entitled. It also takes countless hours to conduct research and to advocate on your child's behalf with the school district, providers, and attorneys. As the parents of a child who struggles with mental illness, your ability to harness resources will be very important in your ability to advocate for your child's best outcome.

Proper Treatment. Treatment for one child may look very different for another child. I keep mindful of this while dealing with Chloe and other families. What is important to focus on is what your gut is telling you. If you're in over your head, seek help through a psychologist, psychiatrist or therapist. If you trust that you can handle the situation and your path, follow it. What I've seen over and over again is that there is no simple answer to treatment and it may change month-to-month or year-to-year. Though it can be extremely challenging, it may be something that needs to be accepted. Just know that what works for one kid may not work for another.

A Supportive School Environment. We were fortunate to have had access to an innovative and progressive charter school that knows how to work with challenging kids. In Chloe's case, a school with small class sizes and a staff that promotes self-awareness and emotional regulation was key to her ability to learn and thrive academically. You may need to be a strong advocate and do substantial research, but an appropriate school environment is vital to your child's success.

> **NOTE:** Depending on where you live in and your financial circumstances, your child may qualify for mental health care, education accommodations and support from your state of residence. You can learn more about your child's educational rights and health care coverage by visiting your state's official website. Medical providers and school administrators should be able to provide you with information as well.

I truly believe that if we can keep creating awareness and sharing information, maybe at some point, mental illness will start getting some resources to make some systemic changes. With my writing and marketing background, I have the knowledge and tools to publish this book and advocate through my blog and speaking opportunities. I'm just starting with baby steps and will keep moving forward to see where it takes me.

We in the trenches don't always feel we have the resources ourselves to handle more than our own child. But we are also the ones who know the unique challenges and the unique joys of life in close encounter with someone with a mental illness. We see the hurdles that are difficult to overcome and it is my hope that in pointing them out together, and in standing in support of each other, we can begin to turn the tide in overcoming the stigma and the shortage of effective and available resources and treatments, and that life on the edge can move a little more towards center.

Until then, know you are doing important work in standing for and loving your children and teenagers, whether they are "normal" or have the unique needs of those with a mental illness.

You are a champion.

Our Stories Go On ...

TREVOR & CAROL (Trevor's mom)

After his stormy history through high school and the justice system, Trevor finally received his GED. Then, in his early 20s, Trevor, who likes to cook, enrolled in a culinary program and got his own apartment. He went to a few classes, but the change overwhelmed him and he began to self-medicate with alcohol, carefully hiding his drinking from his family. When Carol and Paul determined he was living as a recluse, only leaving his apartment to buy food and alcohol, they brought him back to the family home.

While alone there one evening, Trevor frantically called his mother, describing a distraught suicide attempt. He was taken to the hospital and spent three days in intensive care but because he was an adult and couldn't or wouldn't give doctors permission to share his medical information, his parents couldn't even visit him.

When he recovered, they found a treatment program that could deal with his dual diagnosis of social anxiety disorder and alcoholism. When they arrived, he initially refused to go in, but ultimately he completed the 30-day inpatient program.

As part of his continuing treatment, Trevor attended Alcoholics Anonymous meetings, where he met a young woman who also struggles with anxiety and depression, but has been sober for three years. The two now live together a few hours from his parents. Trevor's girlfriend works as a dog walker.

After several unsuccessful attempts to get Trevor Supplemental Security Income, the family hired an attorney whose wife has social anxiety disorder. He had the legal expertise to help them apply successfully, and he understood what the family was dealing with. In a bittersweet moment after meeting with the attorney, Trevor, then 28, told his mom that was the first time he wasn't ashamed of himself and his illness.

Although grief over the limits Trevor's anxiety disorder has imposed on his life ebb and flow for Carol, she has found ways to cope. She sees a counselor regularly, studies Buddhism and exercises.

She has reached out to help people understand anxiety disorders, and, in the process, has found support herself. She overcame her own anxiety to present a half-day workshop on anxiety in children for 60 people, including the staff at the agency where she works, which serves young children with disabilities. Not only did the workshop help professionals look for and understand the disorder, people came to Carol to tell her about similar struggles in their own families.

She hopes to see this openness and support continue to spread.

Carol wonders if someday a better understanding of mental illness and genetics might link all Trevor's symptoms – the primal fear he showed in infancy, poor muscle tone, learning disabilities, anxiety, alcoholism, his susceptibility to common illnesses – into some syndrome.

She knows his struggles are just part of who he is, and she recognizes that some of society's most creative, productive individuals have faced mental health challenges. She hopes to help society understand and support people with mental illness with research and resources.

Until that happens, she's encouraging parents to be advocates for their children and, even more importantly, to support one other and care for themselves while raising a child with mental health challenges.

JOHN & LINDA (John's mom)

For John's mother Linda, the biggest hurdle has been helping John control his anger. He is on medication and they're working with a behavior consultant. They have struggled with stabilizing his mood in order to prevent mood swings from happening. John has a lot of aggression toward Linda, and for a long time she believed he hated her and that they would never connect emotionally. It's hard to fight off her motherly instincts to hug him when he's in the midst of a tantrum.

Through all of her experiences, Linda has learned to view the world differently, and see it as her son does. John doesn't understand prejudice; he sees everyone the same. Linda says John loves strawberry shortcake, My Little Pony and superheroes. She admires his focus and drive.

Linda has had to learn to let go of the image of what her child could be. They may never go to Disneyland, or John may never experience what other kids do, but that doesn't mean there aren't things he will enjoy. There are people she has lost, but she has found others who have helped her, and who share in the baby steps and milestones. She's learned they are not alone, and that what's happening isn't their fault.

When the bad times have come, Linda has celebrated the good times and found encouragement in positive support systems. She also never forgets the good, unique qualities that she sees in her son.

DARREN & AMY (Darren's mom)

With a psychiatric hold from police and the recommendation from the county mental health team, Darren was sent for in-patient treatment at the child and adolescent psychiatry unit. The team identified anxiety, OCD, mood disorder and oppositional defiant disorder as contributors to his mental state and stabilized him. Upon his release from the hospital, he found a place in a group home with a mentor program. A case worker is exploring the potential for placement in a therapeutic foster home.

Amy has spent years with doctors and therapists of her own overcoming the way she had internalized doubts and guilt, assuming Darren's struggles were her fault. Having a trusted mental health partner helped her realize that she hadn't created a monster by spoiling her son. She works to remember that he is ill and she is a good mom, who has worked hard to provide stability and resources to help him.

BRANDON & PAT (Brandon's mom)

Keeping Brandon connected with medical care wasn't easy as he moved between various residential programs and a group home for teens living with mental illness, each in a different county. Determining which county-based coordinated care organization was responsible for paying for his care was still a hassle, and care providers who accept Medicaid are swamped with large caseloads.

Brandon spent about a year in a group home, where he lived with four other young men, coming and going freely as they learned to deal with mental illnesses. After he turned 18, he wanted to try living on his own and taking on greater responsibility for his own health care.

Pat worried that he didn't know how to deal with normal life after spending part of his teen years in institutions instead of with his parents. She admits that it is sometimes hard for the family to figure out whether behavior that seems irresponsible or manipulative is a symptom of Brandon's mental illness or just typical of a teen finding his own way.

After a run-in with the criminal justice system, when an argument spilled onto their front lawn and neighbors called the police, Brandon lived for a time at an Oxford House, a democratically run group home focused on addiction recovery, and back at the group home he'd been part of earlier. In the spring, when he was 19, he returned to live with his parents again.

His girlfriend gave birth to their son in October and Brandon spends time with the baby several times a week. He has become active in a church, attending regularly and finding a supportive community.

He has stopped taking all medications in an effort to be completely drug free, a decision that worried his mother. While she says his mind seems clearer, he is often exhausted by his hallucinations and she hopes to convince him to resume treatment.

She knows he "wants to be a normal guy." While Brandon once dreamed of attending University and playing lacrosse, now the family hopes he can get a job, have money for fun hobbies and build healthy friendships.

Help has come during this process from National Alliance on Mental Illness Family to Family classes. Pat, John and members of their extended family have attended to gain understanding of Brandon's illness, and Pat recommends finding classes or support groups to gain insight into the struggles of a person with mental illness and to find others who understand the challenges for the whole family.

DIANE (Rebecca's mom)

Diane now knows that many pieces of Rebecca's path were laid out before Diane first held Rebecca as an infant in her arms. She learned that the "good girl" who had been pregnant with Rebecca not only used drugs while she was pregnant but was bipolar herself. In fact, the disorder was on both sides of her family and, in addition, Rebecca's biological father's family tree was rife with learning disabilities.

From her new perspective, Diane looks back on years of judgment she felt from others about her parenting skills and understands that they simply didn't know what mental illness means in the lives of families that deal with it. Good friends are still by Diane's side, and they *continue to offer wisdom and support. "You will get to the other side of this," they've told her. "Know there's only so much you can do."*

She went through years of her own therapy to address her sense of loss over the child she expected to raise and her inability to help her daughter. While it is important to Diane to continue to do all she can for Rebecca, she also knows she can't lose her own life in the process. Escape is critical, and for Diane that comes in daily meditation, distance swimming, and art. She has worked to develop the skill of focusing solely on what she's doing.

Diane also joined the board of a nearby mental health facility, where she finds satisfaction in giving back to an organization she's grateful to and where she has access to mental health professionals who continue to advise her on her daughter.

... and CHLOE

As time went by, we saw little changes in Chloe and then, during her stay in her first treatment program, something finally clicked. One night, she called me and said that she'd had an epiphany during a group session. "I saw my bad behaviors and habits in other members in my group," she said. "I don't want to be like that anymore!"

It was music to my ears! She got it! From that point on, Chloe worked hard to redefine herself. After three months of inpatient treatment, she returned home. Everyone—friends, teachers, and neighbors—noticed a difference. "She's a different kid," they'd say. We say she's not a different Chloe, just a better version.

During treatment in Utah at a treatment center that includes an equine component, Chloe's diagnoses have been revised to nonverbal learning disorder (a form of Asperger's), persistent depressive disorder, social anxiety disorder, mathematic learning disorder and ADHD.

We continue to learn how to best parent her and prepare her for life ahead.

Share your story, too, at www.bipolarlemonade.com.

Resources

American Academy of Child & Adolescent Psychiatry (AACAP)
This is a national professional medical association dedicated to treating and improving the quality of life for children, adolescents, and families affected by mental, behavioral, or developmental disorders. The organization's website includes extensive resources for patients and their families, and their programs promote mental health and preventive care through advocacy, education, research, and services. The website includes a child psychiatrist finder here: www.aacap.org/AACAP/Families_and_Youth/Resources/CAP_Finde r.aspx
> **www.aacap.org**
> 3615 Wisconsin Avenue, N.W.
> Washington, D.C.20016-3007
> Phone: 202-966-7300
> Fax: 202-464-0131

Association for Children's Mental Health
A Michigan-based organization, ACMH offers a wealth of resources for families whose children are struggling emotional, behavioral or mental health challenges.
> **www.acmh-mi.org**
> 6017 W. St. Joseph Highway Suite 200
> Lansing, MI 48917
> Phone: 517-372-4016
> Toll-free Parent Line: 888-226-4543
> Fax: 517-372-4032

Bipolar Lemonade
Bipolar Lemonade is a website designed to help provide resources for families struggling with mental illness, and to provide a resource and connection point to reduce feelings of isolation and shame.
> **www.bipolarlemonade.com**

Centers for Disease Control and Prevention: Children's Mental Health.
Extensive website includes overview of mental health disorders, related conditions, symptoms, and treatment as well as data, statistics, and scientific articles.

www.cdc.gov/childrensmentalhealth
1600 Clifton Road
Atlanta, GA 30329-4027
Phone: 800-CDC-INFO (800-232-4636)

Centers for Medicaid and Medicare Services
Part of the Department of Health and Human Services (HHS), CMS provides information for those enrolled in Medicare and Medicaid Services.
www.cms.gov

Child Mind Institute
The Child Mind Institute is an national nonprofit dedicated to transforming the lives of children and families struggling with mental health and learning disorders. They provide resources grouped by topic, for families and for educators to better find the information they need to assist the children in their care.
www.childmind.org

Cyberbullying/Bullying
www.verywell.com/search?q=cyberbullying, or

www.kidshealth.org/en/parents/cyberbullying

Department of Health and Human Services
The Department of Health and Human Services administers more than 100 programs and services that support public health and wellness across the nation.
www.hhs.gov

Eunice Kennedy Shriver National Institute of Child Health and Human Development
NICHD provides research into maternal and child health with a focus on understanding disabilities that occur during human development.
www.nichd.nih.gov

A Guide to Mental Illness and the Criminal Justice System: A Systems Guide for Families and Consumers (NAMI resource)
www.pacenterofexcellence.pitt.edu/documents/Guide to Mental Illness and the Criminal Justice System NAMI.pdf

Lives in the Balance

This non-profit organization was founded by child psychologist Ross Greene, PhD, who originated the Collaborative & Proactive Solutions (CPS) approach to working with behaviorally challenging kids. The organization aims to conduct research, build knowledge, and change the lives of behaviorally challenging kids and their caregivers.

www.livesinthebalance.org
85 Exchange Street, Suite 201
Portland, ME 04101
Phone: 207-210-6589

Mental Health America (MHA)

Dedicated to addressing the needs of those living with mental illness and to promoting the overall mental health of all Americans, MHA operates more than 200 affiliates in 41 states with 6,500 staff members and more than 10,000 volunteers.

www.mentalhealthamerica.net
500 Montgomery Street, Suite 820
Alexandria, VA 22314
Toll-free phone number: (800) 969-6642
Fax: 703-684-5968

National Alliance for Mental Illness (NAMI)

Dedicated to building better lives for the millions of Americans affected by mental illness, NAMI offers free education and support programs in thousands of communities across America. NAMI also provides personal consultation with referrals, information, and support and works to combat stigma through public awareness events and other efforts.

www.Nami.org
3803 N. Fairfax Drive, Suite 100
Arlington, VA 22203
Phone: 703-524-7600
Member Services: 888-999-6264
Helpline: 800-950-6264

National Association of Medicaid Directors

NAMD's mission is to support Medicaid Directors in administering their programs effectively and efficiently across the nation in order to provide necessary health care to those served by Medicaid.

www.medicaiddirectors.org

National Center for PTSD

Part of Veteran's Affairs, the National Center for PTSD website offers information about health and services resources related to PTSD.

www.ptsd.va.gov

National Eating Disorders Association (NEDA)

NEDA supports individuals and families affected by eating disorders and advocates on their behalf.

www.nationaleatingdisorders.org

Confidential, toll-free helpline: 1-800-931-2237

The National Federation of Families for Children's Mental Health

This national, family-run organization focuses on the issues concerning children and youth with emotional, behavioral, or mental health needs and their families. The federation includes more than 120 chapters and state organizations.

www.ffcmh.org

Phone: 240-403-1901

National Institute of Mental Health

NIMH is the lead federal agency for research on mental health disorders. They offer information on a range of topics as well as information on finding health providers, clinical trials, and latest research information.

www.nimh.nih.gov

Toll-free phone number: 1-866-615-6464

Live online chat available

National Sleep Foundation

NSF is dedicated to improving health and well-being through sleep education and advocacy.

www.sleepfoundation.org

The National Suicide Prevention Lifeline

This hotline is free and open 24/7.

1-800-273-TALK (8255)

Sibling Support Project
This organization is dedicated to addressing concerns of brothers and sisters of people with health, developmental, and mental health concerns.

<u>**www.siblingsupport.org**</u>
6512 23rd Ave NW #322
Seattle, Washington 98117
206-297-6368
info@siblingsupport.org

U.S. Department of Labor
The Department of Labor was formed to foster, promote, and develop the welfare of the wage earners, job seekers, and retirees of the United States. Their site provides information about their agencies, and benefits and rights for the U.S. workplace.

<u>**www.dol.gov**</u>
Toll-free phone number: 1-866-487-2365

Recommended Books

The Explosive Child, *Ross Greene*

Lost at School, *Ross Greene*

Raising Human Beings, *Ross Greene*

Helping a Child with Nonverbal Learning Disorder and

Asperger's Disorder, *Kathryn Stewart, PH.D.*

Parenting a Bipolar Child, *Faeda, Austin*

The Behavior Code, *Minahan, Rappaport*

Endnotes

[1] David Crary, "There's a Serious Shortage Of Psychiatrists In The U.S.," *The Huffington Post,* 09/08/2015, accessed at http://www.huffingtonpost.comentry/theres-a-serious-shortage-of-psychiatrists-in-the-us_us_55eef13ce4b093be51bc128f on June 7, 2016

[2] "Child and Adolescent Psychiatry Workforce Crisis: Solutions to Improve Early Intervention and Access to Care," May 2013, accessed at https://www.aacap.org/App_Themes/AACAP/docs/Advocacy/policy_resou rces/cap_workforce_crisis_201305.pdf on January 27, 2019

[3] From NAMI at https://www.nami.org/Find-Support/Living-with-a-Mental-Health-Condition/Understanding-Health-Insurance/What-is-Mental-Health-Parity accessed June 7, 2015.

[4] NAMI, accessed at https://www.nami.org/Find-Support/Living-with-a-Mental-Health-Condition/Understanding-Health-Insurance/What-is-Mental-Health-Parity#sthash.Av5T9bis.dpuf on June 8, 2016.

[5] https://www.nami.org/Find-Support/Living-with-a-Mental-Health-Condition/Understanding-Health-Insurance/What-to-Do-If-You-re-Denied-Care-By-Your-Insurance.

[6] Christina LaMontagne, "How Can I Get My Health Insurance to Pay for Mental Health Treatment?" *The Huffington Post,* 02/09/2015 accessed at http://www.huffingtonpost.com/christina-lamontagne/how-can-i-get-my-health-insurance-to-pay-for-mental-health-treatment_b_6606470.html.

[7] https://www.nami.org/Find-Support/Living-with-a-Mental-Health-Condition/Understanding-Health-Insurance/What-to-Do-If-You-re-Denied-Care-By-Your-Insurance.

[8] The Centers for Medicare & Medicaid Services/CMS.gov accessed at https://www.cms.gov/CCIIO/Resources/Consumer-Assistance-Grants/.

[9] Mentalhealth.gov site provided by the Department of Health and Human Services accessed at https://www.mentalhealth.gov/get-help/health-insurance/.

[10] Mentalhealth.gov site provided by the Department of Health and Human Services accessed at https://www.mentalhealth.gov/get-help/health-insurance/ on June 7, 2016.

[11] Carrie Barron M.D., "Parenting a Difficult Child," *Psychology Today,* Feb 25, 2014

[12] "Types of Parenting Styles and How to Identify Yours," By Bianca Mgbemere and Rachel Telles, December 10, 2013, Vanderbilt University Developmental Psychology blog accessed at https://my.vanderbilt.edu/developmentalpsychologyblog/2013/12/types-of-parenting-styles-and-how-to-identify-yours/

[13] https://www.nami.org/Find-Support/Family-Members-and-Caregivers/Learning-to-Help-Your-Child-and-Your-Family#sthash.Z63y9xmR.dpuf

[14] Greene, Ross, PhD. Lives in the Balance: Changing the Conversation about and with Behaviorally Challenging Kids. www.livesinthebalance.org

[15] Kessler, R. C., Berglund, P., Demler, O., et al. (2005). Life-time prevalence and age-of-onset distribution of DSM-IV disorders in the national co-morbidity survey replication. *Archives of General Psychiatry 62,* 593-602, quoted in "Problems at School," *Association for Children's Mental Health,* accessed at http://www.acmh-mi.org/get-help/navigating/problems-at-school/ on January 27, 2019.

[16] Benoit Daniel-Lewis, "Why Are More American Teenagers Than Ever Suffering From Severe Anxiety?" *New York Times,* accessed at https://www.nytimes.com/2017/10/11/magazine/why-are-more-american-teenagers-than-ever-suffering-from-severe-anxiety.html on January 27, 2019.